DARLINGS OF THE GODS

'How would you like to go to Australia?' LO asked.

Vivien turned round to face him suddenly. Had he gone completely mad?

'For a year . . . Well almost.'

'Australia?'

'The British Council wants the Old Vic to do a goodwill tour. It shouldn't be too onerous. And there's a cruise at either end.'

'Are you serious?'

'My reaction entirely. Until I thought it over. We could do with the time together, Bibs. And the voyage would do wonders for you.'

But she frowned. New emitted a loud 'Miaow'!

'I won't go as your wife. Not as "Lady Olivier".'

'Of course not. We'd lead the company together.'

'I'm not even a member of the company.'

'You leave that to me.' He paused, took a deep breath of the heavy moist air, and grinned. 'So. What do you think?'

'I think . . . I think . . . it would be absolutely perfect.'

This time, instead of New, it was LO who almost began to purr.

About the Author

Garry O'Connor is married and lives with his
wife and their five children in Oxford. Formerly a
director at the Royal Shakespeare Company and
a theatre critic, he is now a full-time writer.

DARLINGS OF THE GODS

A novel based on scripts by Roger Simpson
and Graeme Farmer and on Garry O'Connor's
*Darlings of the Gods: One year in the lives of
Laurence Olivier and Vivien Leigh*

Garry O'Connor

CORONET BOOKS
Hodder and Stoughton

Copyright © 1989 by
Garry O'Connor, Roger
Simpson and Graeme Farmer

First published in Great Britain in
1989 by Coronet Books

British Library C.I.P.
O'Connor, Garry
    Darlings of the gods: a novel
    based on scripts by Roger
    Simpson, Graeme Farmer,
    and on Garry O'Connors
    'Darlings of the gods—one
    year in the lives of Laurence
    Olivier and Vivien Leigh.'
    I. Title
    II. Simpson, Roger
    III. Farmer, Graeme
    823'.914[F]

    ISBN 0-340-50599-0

Printed and bound in Great Britain
for Hodder and Stoughton
paperbacks, a division of Hodder
and Stoughton Limited, Mill Road,
Dunton Green, Sevenoaks, Kent
TN13 2YA (Editorial Office: 47
Bedford Square, London WC1B
3DP) by Cox and Wyman
Limited, Reading, Berks. Photoset
by Rowland Phototypesetting
Limited, Bury St Edmunds,
Suffolk.

Contents

Author's Note

In 1984 I wrote a biographical study called *Darlings of the Gods: One year in the lives of Laurence Olivier and Vivien Leigh*. The year in question was 1948 when Olivier and Leigh jointly led the Old Vic Theatre Company on a tour of Australia and New Zealand, sponsored by the British Council as a sort of public 'thank you' to those countries for the help they gave Britain during the second world war.

The events and tensions of that strenuous tour, and especially as they affected its leaders, is now the subject of a four-part television mini-series, filmed in Melbourne in 1988 by Simpson le Mesurier Films. The mini-series, also called *Darlings of the Gods*, and written by Roger Simpson and Graeme Farmer, has been based on my own book; and the degree of authenticity they have aimed for is shown by Roger Simpson's keeping above his desk a photograph of Laurence Olivier as a reminder that one of the chief protagonists was still alive during the writing of the script, and of the mesmerising quality of his acting. At the same time the television version deliberately concentrates on Vivien Leigh, because it is her dramatic potential that lies at the centre of the story and assists greatly in focussing the events of the tour and a complex set of relationships.

I have now taken *Darlings of the Gods* a stage further. This book is a novel. It follows the series in concentrating on Vivien Leigh – indeed I have, in the way that fiction allows, ventured further into her mind. The dramatic licence this has meant taking with the main elements in the story has, however, been mild. The sources are the same as used in my first book and are, to the best of my knowledge, historically accurate. But to these I have added a certain amount of conjecture – for example, the evidence is contradictory as to whether Peter Finch's celebrated affair with Vivien began in Australia; but their friendship certainly did.

In the novel the character of Laurence Olivier is inevitably going to have less impact than on the screen, largely because I have placed him even more in the shadows. To help establish that sense of distance I have referred to him generally as 'LO'.

I have also been able to add some background detail from the tour, as well as touches offered by my own (first) visit to Australia in 1988.

Two fierce and opposing currents meet in the narrows of perfect love . . . when once they are consummated in marriage it becomes inevitably a perfect hell of storms and furies.

D. H. Lawrence

Prologue

In her nightmare she was lying in a porcelain bath filled with blood. Nearby, lashed to the trunk and low boughs of a tree, was a young virgin, aged about sixteen or seventeen, ready to be sacrificed. She too was naked, her ankles tied together so her legs were neatly compact, her arms spread in the shape of a cross.

Then without warning the pains started. She writhed, she tore at the sheets, she bit her hands. She shouted obscenities, her pretty black hair thrashing wildly about on the pillow. They rushed her to the operating theatre.

Afterwards she came round quickly. Really, it was quite an ordinary miscarriage. But it was not ordinary that she, a healthy young woman of thirty, should have brought on herself such misery. Not to mention the humiliation of it all.

But she was not an ordinary woman, nor were her thoughts – like her nightmares – ordinary when she found herself convalescing in the Dorchester Hotel, to which she had been moved several nights later from the clinic near Marble Arch.

She lay in the most expensive suite in the hotel, in bed, deathly pale, but perfectly recovered from her ordeal. On either side of her bed, and on the dressing table, stood vases filled with the most sweet-smelling and exquisite blooms. Pride of place had been given to a dozen orchids, bred in a hothouse near Welwyn Garden City. On a gold-embossed card attached to them were the words, 'Bad luck, Bibs. We'll try again soonest. Your ever-loving LO.'

Nor was the time ordinary. It was during the middle of

13

the second world war. Outside the windows, covered by heavy velvet curtains, searchlights stabbed at the night sky. The silence was punctured by salvoes of anti-aircraft guns fired from batteries in Hyde Park.

As for her demands, they were not ordinary in any way. She had just telephoned room service and asked for a bottle of champagne to be sent up. Champagne in war time was a rarity. When she heard a tap on the outside door of the ante-room she thought it must be the wine-waiter, arrived to offer an excuse. Some anaemic or spastic boy unfit for military service, no doubt. My God, how the quality of life had gone to pieces. She called aloud for him to enter.

But unseen by her a tall, white-haired gentleman in his eighties had come in, placing his hat upon the stand. He removed his gloves and looked around the lobby, then tentatively knocked a second time, this time on the door of her bedroom.

He was greeted by the most imperious tone the young woman could summon up. 'Who is it. . . ?'

A bomb dropped by a passing German plane crashed into the ground not very far away. Even so, the gentleman was not wholly convinced, and tapped again, perhaps even more softly than before.

'Who *is* it? If you've come to tell me there's no champagne, speak up. I don't care if it's a hundred pounds a bottle, I must have champagne.'

At this, the old gentleman put his exquisitely moulded red face round the door, and she caught at once the twinkle in his eye, the leprechaun arch of the eyebrows, the halo of white hair. She could not bear him to see her thus.

'Oh give me a second or two, darling!' She had not renounced her imperious tone, but it had relented a shade or so. While he waited patiently she leapt from bed, snatched up a dressing gown, and primped with fiendish speed at the mirror. But she clearly considered the damage to her face too great to be rectified in so short a while. 'Oh come in, anyway,' she called out again.

'Lady Hamilton is as brave as her Nelson,' said the old gentleman, whose name was Bernard Shaw and who now emerged into her full view. 'I hear your film has been not only the toast of Churchill, but it's the favourite of Joseph Stalin, too. I'm further informed that viewing it in private has become Adolf Hitler's secret vice. Apparently his troops captured a copy of the film in the Libyan desert.'

'You flatter me, Mr Shaw. Confined to bed by this idiocy while others do their bit. Anyway it's LO they'd all really like to emulate.'

'Spare them a moment's pity – they spend millions of pounds to fulfil their innermost fantasies. Now your husband, yourself – and I, I might add – cost our backers a mere twenty thousand pounds. It would be cheaper to build a thousand theatres in every capital city and allow every man, woman, and child to play the role he or she would care to play – or to pay others to do it for them.'

'How was your homage to the Red Army at the Albert Hall?'

'Boy Scout stuff, I'm afraid. Imagine John Gielgud as the Voice of Radio Moscow. Ralph Richardson wore a gold costume and a high-peaked helmet which made him look like a man from Outer Mongolia.'

The young woman laughed. She could just imagine dear Ralphie looking completely fantastical and out of place.

'It's all very well being a supporter of Stalin in theory, but in practice the display of flag-waving soldiers and sailors singing the Volga boat-song – even led by so distinguished a thespian as your husband – raises in my old heart a forest of contradictory cockles.'

She laughed again. 'By constitution you are incapable of homage!'

'I am afraid so. All too soon vulgarism and barbarity will descend on the world in a scale hitherto inconceivable. Decadence will be freely available to all – like the penny seats at the Old Vic before it was bombed. Yet, unlike the penny seats, the supply will be unlimited. You will have

15

to hold back the tide with your natural good breeding and class which I hear, even now, you are seeking to perpetuate . . .'

'*Was* seeking, GBS.' She stopped. How could he not have known? 'I miscarried three days ago –'

'Oh, I am sorry. I had heard you had been confined to bed with a chill caught while wearing all those nebulous costumes in England's freezing meadows.'

'It seems I'm caught between the devil and the deep blue sea!'

The old gentleman looked disturbed. His sprightly blue eyes grew cold, and a deep, two-pronged claw mark appeared on his brow. 'Don't say Cleopatra was troubling you? The part's foolproof.'

'It's not your film!'

'My film? Please don't call it my film. It bears about as much relation to me as a tiger rug does to a tiger.'

'The director tells me I'm too beautiful to be able to act. I prefer to think I'm too talented an actress just to be beautiful.'

Shaw's forehead grew more composed as he sniffed paradox in the air. He rose to it as an alcoholic rises to the fumes of brandy. 'I would say you are too talented to *need* to be beautiful.' He added quickly, 'And too beautiful to need to be talented.'

But the paradox had no such calming effect on the beautiful young woman, who burst into tears. 'All I wanted was LO's baby – it's all I really ever wanted.'

They turned to view a flurry of gun-flashes through the curtain. Another German plane had been shot down, and exploded in Hyde Park. The woman again experienced a sudden craving for champagne and rang the service bell, continuing, 'Any girl can have a baby, yet why can't I? It's not as if it's been proved medically a rotten womb. It's served me once, why not again? Think how LO would love a baby boy to carry our name. He's such a family man at heart, a down-to-earth, happy-go-lucky fellow, with no complexes at all. All this is confusing and upsetting him!'

Shaw rose and came over from where he was seated, seized her hand, and patted it comfortingly.

'Don't let it upset you, my child. There is always another time. But on the next occasion I would suggest you don't take on anything as lethal as a Shaw role during the pregnancy.'

Part 1

1

In the years following the end of the war London
theatre had begun to revive. The famous Old Vic Theatre
Company had opened again, not in the Old Vic Theatre
in Waterloo Road, where the roof had been severely
damaged by fire bombs, but in the New Theatre in St
Martin's Lane. The careers of London's great actors began
to revive too, especially those of Laurence Olivier
and Ralph Richardson, who had been asked to lead the
new Old Vic Company, together with director John
Burrell.

Vivien Leigh had recovered physically from her miscarriage and completed the film role of Cleopatra in Shaw's
Caesar and Cleopatra. But now, while playing the role of
Anna Karenina in a film of Tolstoy's epic novel, she was
beset by a new strain.

In one scene, that of Anna riding together with her
husband Karenin in a coach along a road through a forest,
memories became threatening. Vivien found herself thinking about the break-up of her first marriage which had
been brought about by her falling in love with her present
husband. As she had been expensively educated – sent as
a child from India, where she lived, to a Catholic convent
in England – guilt about her first husband had always
haunted her.

So when Karenin, inside the carriage, with the sun
piercing the window in dappled patterns, pointed out that
she had, earlier that day at the races, behaved improperly
by showing her sudden concern at the fall of one of the

riders, Vronsky, she remembered once again all the confusion she felt when she was betraying Leigh Holman.

She had no defences – no ordinary self-defence that is – against the guilt to enable her to use the emotion in the role. The situation worsened because the actor playing Karenin was no ordinary ham – unlike the actor playing Vronsky, for whom she felt no emotion at all – but the delicate, sensitive, and extremely real Ralph Richardson, with whose hurt she identified, just as she had with that of Leigh Holman.

When Karenin said, 'I asked you once before to conduct yourself in Society so that evil tongues might be unable to say anything against you. There was a time when I spoke about inner relations: now I do not speak of them', she found herself almost swamped with feeling, and turned away uncomfortably to look out of the window. When Karenin said he was expecting a denial, an apology at least, her inner turmoil became so real that she forgot the script and hardly knew what to say next.

Yet the right words came out as if spoken by someone else. Yes, she confessed, her husband was not in any way mistaken. She had been thinking of Vronsky, and when in the race he fell at one of the fences she had thought her heart would break. She added that she was in love with him and had become his mistress.

But she did not feel any hatred for Karenin. Whoever could for any character played by Ralph Richardson? She had spoken to him flatly, in a resigned tone, but while opening up her face, her memory, her vulnerability to the camera, it had been as if she was giving herself entirely to the act of love. That this was all taking place on a film set had been somehow irrelevant. Her sense of emptiness was real.

She did not notice that in turning away, to choke down the misery Karenin felt at Anna's revelation, Richardson was also hiding deep concern at Vivien's state of mind.

The director, Julien Duvivier, bounced over at the end of the take and came and put his arm around Vivien.

22

'Darling Viv,' he declared, 'that was superb. Let's break for today.'

LO was having no such problems as he extricated his blade from that of the eager young swordsman with whom he was fighting.

'We're ready, sir,' called the first assistant, and they stood back on the set, ready to have a second go. The camera equipment loomed over them; large, cumbersome and made of black metal, it often got in the way. LO still bore the deep scar of a view-finder which had been rammed into his mouth while directing another film, when a horse he could not avoid in time had charged slap into him.

With his hair dyed blond he looked older than his forty years. In this film, *Hamlet*, he was playing the lead. He was also directing the picture.

Olivier looked around the rest of the cast, sure of his mastery, smiling in particular at the adorably pretty young actress cast as Ophelia. He suppressed a ghost of a sigh, which only served to enhance his pleasure – one could not have everything! He loved what he was doing, he relished being at the height of his powers. He enjoyed in particular telling everyone else what to do. Hamlet was an old performance, revived for the thirtieth or fortieth time: he knew the part backwards, he knew every inflection of the verse, every shade of the character's thought.

But to be commanding officer of all this! This was something more exciting and superior.

'To be convincing,' he barked at Laertes, 'you have to enjoy it. You must really go for it.' He crossed the set to speak to the man behind the camera. Next to him stood a stuntman dressed as Claudius, but without wig and head-gear.

'Right. Let's give it a try, shall we?' he said to both of them. He could play the double role easily, even experiencing a fleeting desire to be behind the camera, with the command and arrogant expansiveness of that operator's control.

But the stuntman looked worried, and he parried, with a hesitant look, 'If you're sure . . .'

Reassurance, the imparting of confidence to others, came easily to LO – as did everything else. Like Nelson he was the perfect comforter of dying young midshipmen; like Henry the Fifth, the complete sinew-stiffener for his soldiers.

But he had misunderstood the man who stood before him voicing his doubts. A new appeal to the stuntman's expertise fell flat. For the man was not fearful of any injury he himself might receive. 'It's not me I'm worried about, sir,' he countered. LO placed a reassuring arm on the man's shoulder and brought him a few paces away from the first assistant, who, not wanting to be left out of the conversation, tried to overhear.

'Look, it's not so much a jump as a dive. Just catch me and roll with the movement.' And, catching the look in the first assistant's eye, he then made him party to his whole ambition. 'It's a shot I particularly want,' he affirmed. Almost immediately he was beyond both their concerns, as his mind flew up to the balcony and imagined the effect of the swallow dive he contemplated making from it. A gleeful grin spread over his face.

A tall, straight man with a cool, aloof, utterly untheatrical manner had now slipped into the studio and stood alongside those watching. The actress playing Ophelia he completely dwarfed. She smiled in recognition and he briefly put his arm around her.

'Cecil,' she greeted him.

'Hello, Jean,' he answered.

'You're just in time,' she went on in a tone of importance, as if both knew, not without fear, that a moment they both dreaded but were excited by, was not far off. He raised his head in a half nod, to show he was in tune with what she said.

In the meantime LO had taken up a position on the balcony, twenty feet above the ground. The stuntman, fully regaled in the wig and velvet headgear of Claudius, stood on the ground several yards away from the foot of the balcony, looking up into the air. Behind him, at about a distance of two yards – to the left from LO's position on the balcony top – lay the wounded Laertes, propped up on his right arm. Visible to the camera was a wound on the inside of his left wrist. Beside him on the ground lay his sword.

LO also held a sword, and he too had been wounded, as denoted by a cut in the right sleeve of his shirt. Only a trace of blood was evident. A make-up artist applied last minute tints of flesh to heighten his face, removed the shine with dabs of a powder puff.

'Quiet, please,' ordered the first assistant. 'Stand by for a take. Turn over . . .' A short burst of technical commands succeeded his instruction, ending with the jaws of the clacker-board snapping together: 'Scene two, Take one.'

'Oh villainy! Seek it out,' LO began, while Laertes replied from below:

It is here, Hamlet . . .
The treacherous instrument is in thy hand,
Unbated and envenom'd.
In thee there is not half an hour of life.

Cecil Tennant, next to Ophelia, wore an impassive expression. An ex-Guards officer, now solely in charge of LO Productions Limited, he watched his most valuable asset taking his life in to his own hands. While he had faced up to considerable dangers before this, nothing had quite prepared him for the vicarious thrill of watching a famous actor taking a huge physical risk. The actress playing Ophelia forgot her character, allowed the fear bubbling below the face of Jean Simmons to rise to the surface.

Here I lie, never to rise again. Thy mother's poisoned.
I can no more. The King's to blame.

After the explicit avowal of Claudius's guilt, which the Prince of Denmark had been vainly seeking to establish for nearly three hours, Hamlet could regain the name of action:

The point envenom'd too! Then venom, to thy work.

To this line, above all others in the play, LO knew he could respond with speed and instantaneous feeling. With sword in hand, he now executed a perfect swallow dive on to Claudius below, who, played by the humble stuntman, had the sole function of absorbing the impact of the actor's one hundred and seventy pounds. Valiantly the stuntman deadened the weight, a human cushion, padded and caparisoned as a king.

'Cut!'

The remainder of the cast and the crew applauded spontaneously. Jean and Cecil exchanged heartfelt looks of relief. Jean, embarrassed by emotions she had allowed herself to feel, shrank back into the persona of Ophelia.

'Are you all right, sir?' the first assistant quizzed his leading actor, helping him to his feet. But far from tugging a bruised and shaken Hamlet by the hand, or helping to re-assemble his acting principal, another creature faced him: tyrannical, commanding and quite impervious to physical slight – the film's director. This one was high on adrenalin and asked excitedly, 'How was it?'

'It looked tremendous.'

LO walked away quickly from the scene of his leap, headed towards the view-finder, said eagerly to the director of photography, 'Shall we go for another take?'

As he turned back to scrutinise the balcony, LO became conscious that his buffer lay crumpled with concussion on the ground. Given time, and the concerned attention of those present, the stuntman began to pull himself together. Laertes, no longer dead, sprang to his assistance, holding him up on rubbery legs; while the stuntman swayed backwards and forwards, a small trickle of blood appeared at the right-hand corner of his mouth.

'Somehow I don't think so, Larry,' observed Laertes who, with several others in support, helped steer the stuntman to a nearby chair. LO wandered over to join them. They heard him sigh with genuine regret, although it was unclear whether this was a reaction to the loss of the second take, or out of sympathy for the stuntman.

Cecil Tennant left his observation post at the side of the set and walked firmly over to LO who, at his approach, forgot everything except the pleasure of seeing his old friend.

'Cecil . . .' he responded with heartfelt delight. 'What are you doing here?'

'I've just had some rather good news,' his friend answered. 'From the Palace.'

2

Notley Abbey, an old stone abbey in Buckinghamshire, had been purchased by the Oliviers just a little time before LO began filming *Hamlet*. Part of the building dated from the twelfth or thirteenth century, and had a mysterious, ecclesiastical character. Other parts of the abbey dated from much later, bearing an almost Stuart air – tall ceilings, copious fire-places, winding staircases and priest holes – giving the building both historical resonance and imaginative appeal. Later restoration established a noble and sumptuous unity, nowhere better expressed than in the wide elegant staircase which came sweeping down from the first floor to ground level. Off this, at the head of the stairs, the corridor led to LO and Vivien's bedroom.

The pair, with the looks that created an image of romantic idealism, had some ten or more years before been elevated into the select company of mythologised lovers. Now that these darlings of the gods were together and married, Notley Abbey was their castle. It boasted fine lawns sweeping down to a mill stream. LO, who developed a thirst for gardening, planted a lover's walk of lime and almond. He installed in their greenhouse the newest heating equipment for Vivien to grow tomatoes in latest hot-house style. She had a little sun-house built, too, near the top of the small hill behind the house, where she could retire by herself in the afternoon – and try to grow plump after her repeated bouts of illness.

The couple were holding a celebration in their faerie castle. The abbey shimmered in the moonlight. Vivien had been told that a chapel once adjoined the house and, sure enough, in the barn remnants of stone had been uncovered to reveal the shape of an altar, the curve of a clerestory window. Here the lights were on, for she kept it as a little shrine. For whom or what, who could say?

The mullioned windows in the downstairs rooms were ablaze with light. A black Bentley purred down the long avenue of poplars, crossed the millbridge and pulled up alongside another car parked outside the front door. A butler let in the guests, who were Cecil Tennant and Jean Simmons.

While the butler took their coats, Cecil and Jean waited together in the hall, not quite sure if they would be ushered into the drawing-room, or perhaps shown into the study – both rooms enjoyed almost equal status. Jean, who wore a green silk dress, cowered slightly in the protective shade of Tennant, a frequent visitor to the house.

'Cecil, darling!' a familiar voice rang out above them. They both looked up as Vivien descended the staircase.

Her beauty was exquisite. It glowed. It was a combination, held together in powerful and explosive chemistry of unreality, mystery, loyalty and treachery – but also of discipline, good taste and aspiring virtue. She could appear wise. She had command. She could take a man to the very limit of his capacity for love. But she inspired in the men over whom she cast a spell (which extended to more or less everyone) intoxication rather than sexual passion. Not that both are not closely connected – and one often leads to the other. She was like a goddess-priestess of ancient Crete, equally capable of making a man great, and of destroying him.

Cecil and Jean contemplated her as if she was a vision. Vivien's cunningly shaped low-cut gown showed off her delicate figure to perfection, smoothing out the girlishly round and plumpish bottom – normally skinny, her figure was prone to fluctuation – emphasising the slender moulding of her breasts and shoulders, her long, graceful neck.

The gown was dark red, but covered with sequins, embossed with silver and gold. On anyone else it might have seemed vulgar, but on her it gained a regal power.

'. . . I haven't seen you in ages,' she went on to say to Tennant.

'Nonsense. I was here last month,' he remarked, recovering quickly.

'You spent the entire night with Larry and you know it,' she teased him.

'On business.'

'That's no excuse.'

She reached the foot of the stairs. As if she knew no other way to address the slip of the girl, Vivien stretched out a hand and said grandly, 'You must be Jean.'

Her eyes searched the girl's face like a hawk. She knew of nothing between her and Larry, but jealousy, suspicion, persisted. During the filming of *Hamlet* her mood had worsened. It was absurd. She knew she was too old to play Ophelia. But if this were really so, Larry was too old to play Hamlet. With Ophelia he had been after the real thing. Why not with himself?

The pretty little creature was overawed and almost curtsied. 'It's a pleasure to meet you,' she simpered.

Honestly, it was ridiculous to be jealous of this child. Vivien's mood switched, she became at once warm and gracious. '*Hamlet*'s always been very special to Larry and me. We did it at Elsinore together . . . we had just fallen in love.'

The warmth, the intimacy of recollection, if anything, intimidated Jean more. She was treading on sacred ground, and did not know what to say. She looked down at the yellow carpet.

'Come on. I'll take you in.'

Vivien took her arm, gave her a friendly smile, leading her through into the drawing-room.

Cecil, who had watched the exchange, raised an eyebrow and followed them both in.

*   *   *

30

In the drawing-room Cecil Beaton, a meticulously-groomed costume designer, stood talking by the fire-place with LO. Beaton was a tall, good looking and effete man who wore a flamboyant, red bow tie. He cocked his head to one side when listening. His bright, beady eyes moved restlessly over his host's slim figure.

'The poor man's stunned and bleeding and all I'm worried about is the second take . . .'

Beaton laughed, as did Ralph Richardson, a solidly built figure over six feet tall, who puffed on a pipe. Richardson and LO were best friends – as much, that is, as anyone in the theatre could be said to have a friend, for there was an element of play-acting even in actors' intimacies. But Richardson was real, lacking the disarming love that flows like lava between most actors. He could play the game, too, but he had a reserve of individual hostility, of inquiring fantasy, which he knew how to preserve.

LO noticed the women first, and addressed himself to Vivien, adopting a tone of mock accusation.

'What are you doing with my leading lady?' he demanded.

Vivien's temptingly rounded lips feigned a momentary confusion. She glanced at Jean, then back at her husband. 'I'm sorry Larry, are you asking Jean or me?'

Everything about Vivien delighted Beaton, above all her sharp, wicked personality which contrasted so strongly with her fragile good looks. He laughed appreciatively. So did Ralph, but with an air of abstraction. He was thinking about his parrot, who had just bitten his wife Mu on the ankle and given John Gielgud a terrible fright. He would have to issue a stern reprimand.

LO remained unaffected by Vivien's comment. 'Jean,' he said, quickly moving forward and taking her by the arm, 'come and meet Ralphie . . .' He added, as a throwaway, 'I expect you know Cecil Beaton?'

Vivien found in her hand the comforting shape of a champagne glass, which she raised without thinking to her lips. She sniffed appreciatively at the yellowish vapour that hung over the pale liquid gold before she took a deep sip, allowing the cool thrust of sensation to prickle her throat. She was still watching LO's behaviour with Jean. When she saw Tennant, at her elbow, hoisting his glass in homage to her, she said, 'Fragile, isn't she?' It was the nearest to a compliment she would ever come.

'How's Anna Karenina?' asked Tennant.

'Exhausting.'

'Shouldn't you be easing up a bit?' Like everyone else, Tennant was worried about her health.

She raised her glass to Cecil's. 'Tell that to Mr Korda.'

On the other side of the room Richardson, who following their introduction had taken Jean's hand, found it satisfying to keep it clasped in his.

'Excuse me, but shouldn't you be in bed?' he asked in that light voice of his, as crisp and succulent as onion paper. He turned to LO and, as a humorous idea struck him, smothered a laugh. His face reddened, and he bent his chin into his neck with suppressed merriment. But all he could say was, 'She's so terribly young.'

'As Shakespeare intended,' replied his friend.

'Oh dear boy,' said Richardson, affecting an expression of deep seriousness, but cocking his left eyebrow. 'Been talking to him again, have you?'

At the dinner table the branched candelabra burnt brilliantly and reflected the beauty of swanlike necks and glossy dark hair into several elaborately gilded mirrors on the walls behind. The numbers of guests had been swelled by several more members of the acting profession, even a real noble or two, who were put in the shade by LO and Vivien. The old aristocracy were becoming resigned to being stripped of their social power by the new dukes and moguls of show business, and had abandoned their traditional hunting grounds and gaming tables to join them at film festivals and gala evenings.

It was a lively, jolly dinner, with a lot of banging of glasses, shouts and laughter. Beaton rose to make a speech, his tone as polished as his words were carefully chosen.

'Dear friends,' he said. 'When Ralph Richardson received his knighthood earlier this year, our joy and delight were diminished only by the fact that his closest friend and colleague was somehow overlooked. When one marries a second time, it seems, one must expect to do a little penance.'

Beaton stood roughly half-way along the table. At the end furthest from LO sat their hostess, who responded, drunk as she now was, with a wicked and strongly audible aside, 'I've never been called that before!'

The force of her unfinished personality in contrast to her perfect beauty arrested everyone. Even the most sceptically-minded person there had to admit her vulgarity had class. She won a round of laughter.

'And so, my friends, a toast, to a quite remarkable man. Actor, producer, film director, theatre manager, administrator and celebrated Englishman, Laurence – soon to be Sir Laurence – Olivier.'

LO jumped up for his own quick thrust. 'Cecil, you are very kind, but wait for the investiture, please.'

'A formality, surely,' said Tennant.

'Yes, but wonderful theatre.'

More laughter. But Vivien did not laugh. She was thinking of the profoundly depressing scene in *Anna Karenina* when Anna suspects that Vronsky no longer loves her . . .

LO was now responding to the toast at length. 'My dear friends. It is I who should be toasting you. To my darling wife . . .' He held up his glass to Vivien (who responded almost without thinking, with, 'And little penance') 'without whose love and fortification . . .'

Several of the company gave the appropriate fruity responses to such risqué references.

'. . . I would have achieved but nought. To my business partner,' he raised his glass to Tennant. 'To the best designer in England,' he raised to Beaton. 'To fellow actors,' he raised the glass this time to Jean, who beamed him a ravishing smile. 'And fellow rogues,' by this he meant Ralph and the others, 'thank you for attending this very special night . . .' He regarded them with a straight face, and then spoke with playful vanity. 'The pun was intended . . .'

The infectious quality about actors on such public occasions was that they could, without any qualm or reserve of manner, vocalise and amplify their importance. How they groaned, and laughed – as needed.

'I would like to say, most sincerely, that this is in no way a personal accolade . . .'

Vivien stared down at her glass. It was empty. But then, mercifully, someone topped it up. She had to admit that her influence over LO had been beneficial, had at times even added a heroic dimension to what he had done – she assumed that he was meaning her . . .

'But that would be untrue . . .' Vivien watched the smiles of appreciation suddenly vanish from the faces of Tennant and Jean, although laughter greeted this new remark of his. 'It is a personal tribute, and rightly so, for I did it on my own, without any help from any of you . . .'

She had to tell herself that he was clowning, that he loved a good practical joke or leg-pulling! But what if he really meant it? Or what if one really stopped knowing if anything he said was real, because he acted all the time? Did he himself know when he was acting and when he was not?

'He's going to be impossible,' she heard Cecil Beaton say.

'I'm sorry,' he concluded, 'but that's the way it is . . .'

Look at him now. Had it not been her driving ambition and her belief in him which had sustained and carried him along the path to success? She had broken down his innate shyness and reserve with strangers; she had educated his tastes. She had even changed his appearance from an uncouth youth with unruly black hair and yobbish eyebrows into the well-groomed dream of every middle-class schoolgirl and the harmless fantasy of every lovesick wife. She had taught him to entertain.

Now they had all broken away from the table and stood in groups. Ralphie was putting his arm around LO. Beaton had been joined by Tennant. They were chatting about the effect of LO's knighthood on the politics of the Old Vic Company. Beaton observed cattily that what with both Olivier and Richardson now knighted the rest of the governing board would hardly be very pleased. Tennant, soothingly, commented that they should be. Beaton went further, saying they would be green with envy.

Vivien, now virtually alone at the table, heard herself being appealed to, 'And what do you think, Vivien? Has he been a clever boy?'

She breathed in. She had not drunk that much. She answered, in a sharp witty tone, 'It seems a shame his career is over.'

'What do you mean?' inquired Beaton, almost savouring the taste of wickedness.

'Well,' she said, 'knighthoods are for retired politicians and senile judges. What need have actors of such silly honours?'

'He can hardly turn it down,' she heard the more reasonable tones of the other and more business-like Cecil interposing.

She decided to make a bold joke at Larry's expense. Aiming her remark directly at the others she said, roguishly, 'Certainly not, having sought it so eagerly . . .'

They laughed. There was such a fine line – if any line at all – between what people laughed at, or found offence in. The line was drawn entirely with tone and gesture.

'What about Ralph?' asked LO, who had heard and was laughing uproariously with the others. 'You didn't mind when he accepted.'

'Yes, but Ralphie doesn't take it seriously.'

But now what did all this mean? Did Vivien herself know? If she had wanted to undermine admiration, she could not have gone about it more stealthily or ambiguously.

'There's not a man or woman in England who won't applaud the decision,' said Tennant stolidly.

'There's one,' said Vivien. 'But who's counting?'

'Vivien – I do believe you're jealous,' laughed Beaton.

'I'm jealous of his talent, if that's what you mean.' And at the very last, when it seemed too late, she played up to the occasion – this time unconsciously – delivering her next remark with forceful sincerity. 'Isn't everyone?'

She had contributed some words of flattery with which everyone could agree, and, more than this, feel comfortably soothed that she had added her seal of official approval to the honour granted to him. That they were true words, uttered from the depth of her being, no one much noticed. She could, with a hundredth of the effort, have passed a dozen superficial compliments. But she had to be herself.

Olivier smiled at Vivien to acknowledge her tribute. Jean, totally beguiled by the electricity flying backwards and forwards between this pair, gazed on them both in wonder.

3

LO had seen off all his guests. The last to leave had been
Ralphie, who was giving Jean a lift in his convertible. The
two men had been very merry, while the girl sat in the front
seat, eyes lowered, waiting for the badinage to subside. LO
slipped and nearly fell on the gravel. Really, they had all
been more than a little plastered.

Back inside the house he discovered Vivien pouring
herself a generous brandy. He pulled himself together,
straightened his coat, then his collar, lifted a hand towards
her.

She knew he was there, although she did not turn. She
longed for his hand on her shoulder. Couldn't he simply
come up to her, place his body up against hers? Why the
hell did they need to speak so much? Words, words, words
– they came between, made themselves a nuisance.

'Darling, you don't need another drink.'

He did not have to say it, make her feel she was a child,
unable to be responsible for herself.

'I do. I feel dreadful,' she answered, just like a child.

'Then for heaven's sake, go to bed.'

There he was, sending her to bed like a child – just like
her mother used to do. At least Father would never pack
her off to bed, but dandle her on his knee, as if she was
one of his conquests. She would try to appeal to him,
woman to man.

'You're not going to bed?' she asked.

'I've some things to do.'

'Like what . . .?'

'Letters to write . . . phone calls . . .'

Oh yes. All that. She knew only too well. Since that letter had arrived from the Palace it had not stopped. This was what frightened her.

He was no longer driven by her, or even by himself – something had taken him over and drove *him*. This something else, she did not exactly know what it was, it frightened her. She feared she was losing him. And if it went on, what would happen to this humble clay Galatea moulded by her Pygmalion? She would be smashed to pieces!

'I'm not worried about you. I'm lonely. Come to bed . . . Your precious knighthood can look after itself.' Having started in this way, having, so to speak, gone over to the attack, her discontent fed on itself – or, rather, on the business he had been trying to attend to so late at night.

'Letters and phonecalls. To whom? To newspapers? To let them know you're doing interviews?' She could primp and cavort about like a tart when she wanted to, and now she did so, with scornful, mock pomposity. 'Sir Laurence Olivier is receiving the press . . . Provided they address him correctly. Anything before page three. Front page preferred.'

She was watching him for a reaction. But nothing came. Only the fixed gaze. None of her mother's violence that she was trying to provoke, the exaggerated Catholic guilt which, because her mother had beaten it into her, she was trying to arouse in him. Not that it was real guilt, positive guilt, which might lead to activity and change; rather a crushing sense of shame.

'If you really want to make the headlines, then turn down the honour.' She put on the voice of a broadcasting announcer. 'Actor stands on principle – nothing but the House of Lords.'

Still he said nothing. No expression on his face gave away anything he could be thinking. If it had revealed any sign of weakness, any scorn or anger, with what a sledge-hammer of self-concern it would have been met by Vivien.

Frustrated now, as much by his failure to respond to her as by his acceptance of the knighthood, she could merely burst out, with an almost petulant ring of defeat, 'It's a stupid, empty accolade . . . And nothing to do with an actor's work . . . And I don't want to be known as Lady Olivier.'

At this, but still with perfect control – although perhaps with an edge of sharpness, and even a slight flickering of resignation playing about the thin-lipped mouth, he said, 'Nobody's suggesting that, dear.'

Cheated of her explosion, Vivien found herself on the point of tears. But sooner than cry, than give in, become the weak woman that he could safely patronise and comfort, she flung down her glass and hurried from the room.

LO returned to his silent watchfulness.

She waited for him. But he had not come. Now she lay in bed, dressed in a simple white nightdress. She had been crying.

She had so preferred it earlier in their lives when all obstructions to their passion had been outside themselves. Like Paris and Helen of Troy they had been kept apart as a result of others conspiring against them. They had suffered torments of separation and uncertainty. They had always looked forward to when they could marry. Even their adultery had been given some kind of dignity – a kind of sanctity – by the purity of their love for one another, their desire not to hurt those close to them – his wife and child, her husband and child – no less than to hurt each other.

But now the obstacles were in themselves, their obstinacy, their self-regard.

'Here. I've made you a lemon drink . . . A good sleep and you'll feel fine.'

He stood at the bedroom door, with a steaming drink on a silver platter. She wanted to laugh. Good old caring

39

male. Pull yourself together, gal, have a good night's sleep, and by jove you'll feel better in the morning.

'Stop being so understanding,' she told him, which he believed to be his cue to move in behind her and act the romantic lover, touch her tenderly and kiss her on the forehead. She turned beneath him, put her arms around his neck. 'You'll kill me with your kindness, you really will.'

He did understand – at last. He smiled. Could she be sure of him?

'I love you, Larry.'

'And I love you.'

'I'm sorry.'

He leaned over and placed his arms around her, kissed her more ardently, wanting to be carried away to rediscover the safe old rhythm of heroic passion.

'I hate that wretched Anna . . .'

'Puss . . .'

'Waiting all the time to die . . .'

He sighed. 'Darling, it's only a film.' He sat up and then backed slightly away from her on the bed, readjusting to reality again.

'Does all love have to be paid for with pain?'

He frowned. Somewhere inside him lurked the boring, literal-minded Englishman.

'Vivien . . .' he half remonstrated.

'Can we go away when it's over?'

He smiled again, this time indulgently. 'Of course we can.'

That he was speaking to her as if to a child really did come across this time.

'Somewhere warm and friendly . . . Just the two of us . . . ?'

'We'll see, Bibs . . .'

'I do so want us to be happy.'

'Darling, we are. Now, go to sleep.'

He kissed her again, this time as a father kisses his daughter – chastely, protectively.

*   *   *

40

As LO slowly descended the stairs from his and Vivien's bedroom it never crossed his mind that his passion for Vivien might be dying. All through life, it seemed, his capacity for love had not found its full expression. He could never love his mother enough because she had died when he was still only a small boy. His marriage to his first wife had denied his overwhelming need to love both its sexual and its emotional outlet. And, for all the passion and excitement he had experienced with Vivien, marriage had yet to result in any satisfactory outward expression of their love.

What had happened with Vivien was that he had experienced a fantastic explosion of love inside him which he had put into his work instead of his marriage. A selfish direction for it to take, some might say. The risks undergone with Vivien, the guilt and agony shared, the suffering he accepted as giving him knowledge and experience, had in one sense paid off. He had learned to love his work – and the characters he was playing.

He had arrived down in the drawing-room once more. Noticing the pieces of shattered glass on the floor, he stooped and recovered some of the fragments. He placed the broken pieces on the marble mantelpiece. Then, for several moments, he simply stood there, deeply lost in thought and feeling weary.

After a while he grew aware that he was facing himself in the mirror, but also that he had not looked at himself once all the time he had been standing there.

He turned his eyes on himself, lifting his head slowly so that his image unrolled from the mass of dyed blond hair down to his shiny Church's shoes, until he was standing almost above himself looking down. Then he moved closer to the mirror, as if to examine himself almost pore by pore.

Was he looking for signs of the advancing years – the blemishes and wear of a life spent in grease-paint? Was he worried about the rigours of life with Vivien? About current or future prospects or about the governors of the

Old Vic? About whether he would have enough money on which one day to retire?

At last he spoke – softly, but with carefully placed emphasis.

'Your Majesty, you honour me too greatly . . .'

He made a solemn and profound bow.

4

In the offices of the New Theatre, in St Martin's Lane, where the Old Vic board had been hastily convened, Tyrone Guthrie was holding up a London evening paper whose headline blazed 'Laurence Olivier and Malcolm Sargent at Investiture'. Below the headline was a photograph of the newly knighted pair, both in morning clothes, Sargent bright and smiling, LO lined and exhausted. What a strange contrast LO's attire made to his blond, Hamlet hair.

Guthrie was a tall, pin-headed man of military bearing with a thin moustache, and a short army haircut. He wore no coat, a bright red tie, and a short-sleeved, bright blue shirt which emphasised his large, bony structure. Out of sight, beneath the table, were the sand shoes he invariably put on because more conventional footwear pinched his large, flat feet.

He awaited, with complete assurance and sangfroid, the arrival of Lord Esher, an aristocrat who had occupied himself without much understanding in the affairs of the theatre. He had taken over the job of leading the governors since the death of the former chairman, Lord Lytton. Lytton had been a cheerful sympathetic soul.

Esher, an icy and ambitious man of sixty-seven, arrived. He wasted no time in reviving his annoyance over the knighthood. Tossing down his hat and gloves on the boardroom table – dress accessories that Guthrie acknowledged with a somewhat camp condescension – he said, 'So now it's officially "Sir Laurence"!'

Guthrie had a brisk schoolmasterly manner with a suggestion of latent homosexuality about it. He tended to look down his nose when he talked.

'One might be forgiven for thinking there were more titles among the directors than on the board.'

Esher looked at Guthrie, aware that he, too, deserved more recognition. The man had given the Old Vic far more years of service than either Olivier or Richardson.

'Well, I suppose it's good for the theatre.'

'With respect, Lord Esher, I prefer directors with more commitment to the company.'

'We can hardly complain about that,' said Esher in a disbelieving tone, as if inviting Guthrie to challenge the statement, which Guthrie did at once.

'Well, I hear Richardson's already been given twelve months leave of absence. To go to Hollywood.'

'Has he?'

'This is all rather difficult, because I had the impression he was off to Australia.'

'Why don't we send Burrell?'

'He hardly has the right image, while his disablement won't stand all that travelling. He had polio, you know. The British Council needs a bigger name. This is a goodwill tour, after all. "Thank you Australia for all you did in the war." They'd never accept Burrell.'

'Then who?'

'Perhaps Richardson shouldn't go to Hollywood.'

'Of course if he were to resign and be replaced . . .'

'By whom?'

Guthrie, who could conjure up a kind of unworldly whimsicality, stared out of the window, as if his next statement contained nothing but pure altruism. 'By someone more committed. To the theatre, I mean . . .'

Esher masked a smile with his hand. 'You could go.'

Guthrie feigned surprise.

Damn it, thought Esher, when Guthrie then declined the suggestion, although was at pains to emphasise how much he liked Australia. Did Guthrie have other ambitions? What did the man want? So he put forward the idea of Olivier. Guthrie shook his head.

'I doubt if he'd go,' he said. 'He's much too important. Especially now.'

'Well hang on a moment, Guthrie,' Esher insisted. 'After all, we are the board.'

'Yes,' said Guthrie in his most nasal tone. 'Well, that's the problem, isn't it? The directors do what they like.'

'What if he takes his wife with him,' said the wily Esher. 'The idea might seem more attractive.'

'But she's not even a member of the Old Vic Company,' objected Guthrie. 'She'd have to be appointed over the heads of others.'

'They would make an excellent pair of ambassadors.'

'Celebrated ambassadors . . .' Guthrie stroked his chin. 'For the English theatre – or for themselves?'

5

She did not know why, exactly, but one day when she had a few hours off from *Anna Karenina* she commandeered the studio car and called without warning at the studio in Denham where LO was filming *Hamlet*.

LO had not been home the previous night, for he had become so heavily involved in every side of the production that he just could not give it up, and worked well into the small hours.

Although the rational side of Vivien told her that there was nothing to worry about, that LO's full concentration was upon the film – and that he was not in any way straying from the task he had set himself – there was a side of her which was becoming increasingly irrational.

The compensation for not playing Ophelia that she had received from Alexander Korda, namely the part of Anna, had not really worked. The trouble was she knew, at the back of her mind, although no one had ever mentioned it to her, that it was LO who had, as a special favour, asked Korda to give her the part. It gave her the resentment of the controlled woman.

What exactly had she expected to find by calling in at Denham? LO and his leading lady in one another's arms? She knew that they were not, but still the idea persisted. She stood at the back of the crowded viewing theatre while the production team and camera crew watched the day's rushes. In the scene between Ophelia and LO Vivien searched for signs of his betrayal of her. But there were none.

Of what, exactly, was she jealous? Of her own youth which had gone? Of someone else acting with LO and reaping all the glory and attention? Of the fact he spent so much time with his work – that he had no time for her? This was patently absurd, for she had such a big career of her own.

LO was so enjoying the process of filming *Hamlet* that even her midnight telephone calls to the studio did not divert his energy or attention. He worked with superhuman effort, but easily, even with energy to spare; but he did not respond to the increasing number of signals she gave that all was far from being well.

The filming of *Anna Karenina* could no longer provide the safety valves she needed. She felt more and more confined and pulled around. The corsets that had to be lashed up tight with their inhuman strings, the gorgeous, but complicated costumes so lavishly designed by Cecil – even the gloves – seemed constricting. She bawled out her wardrobe assistants and dressers, she ripped off buttons, she kept everyone waiting on the set with her last-minute demands, she even quarrelled with Beaton.

Cecil went to complain to Richardson, the only person on the film with any real authority. Richardson despaired of the director managing to control her. In any case, Duvivier usually seemed more concerned with the effect of his lights on the faces he was filming than with what those faces were actually trying to portray.

Richardson went to try and reason with Vivien. He discovered, to his surprise, that even her dressing room had taken on some of the characteristics of disorder into which she was beginning to slide. Instead of the raw and powerful 200 watt bulbs supplied for the make-up mirrors she had substituted a standard lamp behind the chair. The bulb could not have been more than twenty-five watts, and the lamp had a frayed and frilly shade.

But when he arrived she was not even sitting in front of the mirror.

'Please, don't turn on the light,' she cried from the other

side of the room, where she crouched in the shadows. Richardson was shocked. Her voice had lost its warmth and colour. He noticed some photographs lying on the low table beside her – publicity stills for the picture, taken by Cecil Beaton himself. They were torn and defaced, and one of them had a sharp fingernail scratch across it. Could there have been anything more touching or alluring than Cecil's images of a woman in the fullness of her early maturity yet still kittenish, still soulful and completely captivating? Had she considered the photographs carefully she would have known why she could no longer play Ophelia. Shakespeare's part was essentially that of an empty sweet girl, out of her depth, a creature who existed purely on a level of fantasy – both for herself and for the prince she thought she loved. Anyone who acted her had to project an unreality of feeling.

But Anna was real, she was mature. She had to plan, make decisions, take responsibility for her love for Vronsky. Ophelia's death was irresponsible and pathetic, but Anna's death was a direct consequence of the exercise of her conscious will. She knew what she was doing. She could have resisted her fate, she had the wisdom and intelligence to know the folly she was committing. In the novel, therefore, she won and kept the reader's sympathy.

All this had somehow passed Vivien by.

'Please don't turn on the light,' she repeated.

'We've been waiting for you for over an hour,' said Ralph. 'There's some problem with the wretched lights, but they'll fix it soon enough. You really should be on set . . .'

She smiled with genuine affection for Ralph's familiar, caring tone.

'I've been going through the publicity shots. They're simply dreadful. They make me look a hundred and three.'

Richardson tried to scrutinise her face where she sat cross-legged in the corner of the room. When he could see her more clearly he could make out the lurid sticky mess she had daubed on her mouth with lipstick, the doll-like blobs of rouge painted on her cheeks. She had been crying and her tears had smudged the effect she had been trying to achieve.

6

It was a beautiful sunny summer afternoon at Notley when the car brought Vivien home from the film studio. Wasps buzzed around the dark car as it swept up the gravel drive and drew to a halt in front of the oak and metal front door.

Vivien had not recovered from the day. Although she had changed into an organdie, full-skirted dress, and made some obeisance to the sunnier weather with a large-brimmed straw hat with a blue band hanging down the back, her mood of self-pity had remained unbendingly black. She wore sunglasses with white rims. Richardson had persuaded her to remove all traces of make up.

She leant on his arm for the few yards from the car to the front door, and he almost had to carry her up the stairs as they ascended from the baronial lower level of Notley to the light and airy bedrooms. He left her to undress in her own room and went downstairs to wait for the doctor, whom he had already called. Waiting for him for ten minutes or so he grew impatient, and when the doctor arrived, he led him upstairs at once.

Half an hour later the doctor had left, but LO had now returned from Denham, apologising profusely for not having arrived sooner. He and Richardson went to the bedroom together, to see that Vivien was comfortable. Richardson told LO that the doctor had given her a seda-tive and that she would be asleep twelve hours or more. The doctor had told him it was simply a case of nervous exhaustion. Richardson said he would wait downstairs and left LO with his wife.

When Ralph had gone LO moved over towards the bed where Vivien lay asleep. The sheet and blankets had slipped from the bed where she lay on her stomach and her nightdress hardly spread as far as to cover the top of her thighs, which were parted vulnerably. He stood over her, watching for some moments.

On the bedside table stood a bottle of sleeping pills and an empty glass. He reached out and drew the covers over her.

'What she needs is a complete holiday,' Ralph was saying to LO. 'You both do.'

They were walking in LO's folly, an avenue of hazel trees on one side, lime on the other, which curved off to the left and down to the mill stream. It was known as 'The Walk Where You Will'. Both men held glasses of wine.

'Who has the time for that?'

'Have you thought about Australia?'

'I beg your pardon?'

'Well, now that I'm going to America, you could lead the tour to Australia.'

'No thank you.'

'A long sea cruise. A year away. It would do Vivien the world of good.'

'It's a hell of a holiday.'

'Not if she's your leading lady.'

'Now come on, Ralphie. The board would have a fit. "Hasn't got the classical credentials old boy."'

'She has the drawing power. She's a star.'

They had reached the end of the walk. The twilight was darkening. A slight breeze was rising off the stream.

'You're worried about her, aren't you?'

Ralph certainly was. It was he who had told Duvivier to call off the filming for the rest of that day. When, in her dressing room, he had tried to calm her down, she had treated him to a jealous outburst about LO's Ophelia, then demanded of him, in a tone of extreme self-pity, that if she was twice her age had she not at least half the looks?

The worst moment had come when she'd complained, in a fragile and brittle voice, that she could not find matches to light her cigarette. Illuminated by his match, the sight of her face had made him almost jump with fright. The stark, mask-like image of her face. The painted, doll-like fragility.

'Aren't you?' Richardson asked his friend.

'Yes . . . and no. I'm not surprised. She tries too hard. At everything.'

Richardson shook his head. 'You spend so little time together. And you know she misses you terribly.'

LO began to sound exasperated. 'We can't do *everything* together Ralph . . . I'd be exhausted.'

Richardson stared at him, wondering what his friend was hinting at. Hadn't there been a period, he remembered, when LO and Vivien had first been together and LO had been complaining that he could not learn his lines. 'Too much time in the sack with Viv,' he had told his friend. 'You'll have to give up sex for four or five days.'

'What's that got to do with it?'

'Phosphates in the brain,' Richardson had replied. 'You shot all yours and it's phosphates that retain the memory.'

LO was peering into his face.

'Australia?'

'Oh.' Ralph came back to the Walk Where You Will. He said, reassuringly, 'Let's talk about it Larry, over dinner.'

Dinner was at the Athenaeum in London where they ate smoked salmon and quail and drank several bottles of the club's claret.

Richardson's suggestion of Australia had already caught fire in LO's mind, so he started outlining schemes and ideas, and even drew up a list of productions they could take on tour. He might, to begin with, revive *Richard III*, his most famous role. Vivien could play Lady Anne. She had already proved herself as the sexy Sabina in *The Skin of our Teeth* by Thornton Wilder, and he knew how happy she would be to play her again. As for the third play – and he knew there should be three – they needed a classic which gave them parts of equal weight.

'What about *School for Scandal*?' said Ralph.

'Not a bad idea, Ralphie.'

When, having regaled each other liberally with port, they left the dining-room, Richardson managed – and he was not quite sure how it came into his possession – to be carrying a bottle of champagne. He found the doorman eyeing him as they were being helped on with their coats. To some extent the club tolerated Richardson's eccentric activities – his ordering, for instance, of a jam omelette one day at lunch, even his arrival, one evening, with his parrot José on his shoulder and whom he insisted on taking through to dine with him.

But the doorman was eyeing the champagne with particular disapproval.

'Ah Morton . . .' said the senior knight. 'Now you may have noticed I'm holding a bottle . . .' He gave Morton the champagne to hold. 'Which, under the rules of this establishment, I must not carry from the premises.'

'Unfortunately, sir. Rules is rules.'

'Which is why I'm going to hand it to my friend here . . .' Ralph retrieved his bottle and handed it to his friend. '. . . to carry for me.'

'Regrettably, Sir Ralph, the rule is not limited to members.'

Richardson looked crestfallen. 'Oh . . . it's not?'

'Regrettably,' said Morton.

'You mean *no one*, Morton – I can call you Morton, Morton?'

'Of course, sir,' said Morton, a touch frostily, feeling threatened. He could not remember the other man's name, and wanted to tell his wife he had seen him. Sir Cedric Hardwicke, was it?

'You mean *no one*, Morton, can carry liquor from the premises?'

'That is the rule, sir. Licensing you understand.'

53

LO pulled a face, gestured defeat and handed Richardson back the bottle. The two men could sense coming over them their incorrigible desire to perform a double-act. Sometimes, in the past, when they were together on stage, LO would try to 'corpse' his friend, although sometimes Richardson was better at it than anyone, for no one could ever know if he was doing it deliberately or not. One night, when Olivier was playing Iago, Richardson Othello, LO had written in black eye-pencil on his right eye-lid, 'F---' and on his left eyelid 'Off!' and when the pair had had a particularly eye-ball to eye-ball exchange had winked first the right eye, then the left. Richardson had doubled up to silence his laughter.

'Then that presents us, Morton, with something of a problem . . . A problem we must face with initiative.'

'And ingenuity?' said LO.

'Precisely,' said Richardson.

The old club retainer regarded them with suspicion.

'And so, if I cannot carry the bottle from the premises . . .'

Richardson lightly threw the bottle to LO.

'And if I, Morton, am similarly constrained . . .' said the other actor.

He tossed the bottle back to Richardson.

'Then we must be scrupulously careful.'

The bottle was now back in LO's hands. He had nattily caught it from a low lob behind Morton's back.

'Scrupulous and careful . . .'

The bottle was again in Richardson's hands. He was now also the other side of Morton and near the door.

'To ensure that it is not *carried* . . . Whoops!' At this he almost dropped the bottle, '. . . from the premises . . . at all.'

While the champagne had been moving constantly from hand to hand, LO had hopped down the entrance steps to the club and out into the street. With one final looping throw Richardson impelled the bottle through the doorway arch, where, on the pavement the other side, it was deftly fielded by LO.

'Good night,' said Richardson to the stupefied Morton.

LO then drove like a maniac, thrusting Richardson's Aston Martin over dark country crossroads towards Notley, overtaking blindly on corners, and trying, on the few miles of dual carriageway here and there, to give the car wings. LO thrilled to the car's power and speed.

Richardson, who liked, he would be the first to confess, his daily fright, had already had enough for that day. He held his hat with one hand and gripped the champagne bottle with the other. As it began to grow light, Richardson noticed a car looming up ahead at an intersection, and pointed it out to LO who, instead of drawing back, decided he could beat it. A collision seemed inevitable, but LO just squeezed ahead of the other car which sounded its horn in noisy protest. Richardson shot his head round to look sideways at his friend; his own knuckles were white.

A couple of hours later Richardson was eating breakfast. He still wore evening dress, although it and he looked somewhat the worse for wear. LO joined him, his black tie dangling from his lapel pocket.

'How is she?' asked Richardson.

'Still dead to the world,' said LO. 'The doctor must have prescribed a heavy dose.'

He eyed with approval the generous helpings of steaming eggs, bacon and meadow-fresh mushrooms the housekeeper was doling out to them. But Richardson looked at him severely.

'Laurence,' he said, 'for as long as I live I will never forgive you for that piece of driving.'

'Listen who's talking,' said LO with a merry laugh.

'Ah, but as a passenger I have other standards.'

'Ralphie,' barked LO, his voice preparing to shoot into one of its famous accelerated runs of consonants. 'When you encounter a moment of great danger you must pass over it as quickly as you can.'

Richardson swallowed a succulent morsel of bacon. 'You must be hell to live with.'

'Oh, we manage,' said LO a little less confidently.

Richardson saw his chance to raise the subject he had been meaning to broach all night.

'She's a very special woman, you know.'

LO's eyes misted over. 'Yes – she is.'

'A delicate flower.'

'Oh, is she?'

'You must be very, very careful with her.'

'She'll get over it, Ralphie. She's a lot tougher than she looks.'

'I'm not talking about her stamina, Larry. Or her tuberculosis.'

LO put down his knife and fork. What was Ralph on about now?

'This film,' continued Richardson. 'It hasn't been a good idea.'

'Why ever not?' LO frowned with incomprehension.

'It's as if she associates too closely with the role she's playing. At times she's not just acting Anna – she *is* Anna.'

LO now understood and replied simply, 'People don't seem to realise, she's a very talented actress.' He picked up his knife and fork and went on eating.

'No. It's too chillingly real. Her guilt. Her conscience at betraying her husband. Her morbid obsession with penance – and death.'

LO wondered what on earth had now seized his friend. Ralph's great imagination had really caught fire. He smiled indulgently at the sinister picture he was painting, but forgave him completely.

'Really Ralphie . . .'

'It's as if every day she's reliving' – he hesitated before saying it, then turned to face LO – 'leaving her husband and child.'

'What? For me?'

'She betrayed them, old boy.'

'What is this? A sermon on morals?'

'It affects her deeply.'

'She was brought up a Catholic.'

'Don't dismiss it, Larry. Whatever you do, don't dismiss it.'

LO studied Richardson without comment. With curiosity rather than concern.

'You don't believe me?' said Richardson with a ring of sadness in his voice.

'Oh yes, I believe you. Up to a point . . . But you're only seeing a part of her. She's a very complex woman.'

'No doubt.'

LO spoke with pride. As if she was his own creation. 'Incredibly so . . .' He rounded out with spontaneous energy each item on his list, 'Wife, lover, mother – whore.' Richardson sat back in his chair, contemplating the qualities of his friend's wife. 'Lady of the Manor,' continued LO, 'petulant child . . . seductress.'

Richardson swallowed. He would have been the last to deny that Vivien attracted him sexually.

'There's madness there, if that's what you mean. Things you wouldn't believe.'

'Tell me . . .' LO had aroused his curiosity.

'No, it's personal.'

'I swear, I'd not tell a soul.'

LO shook his head disapprovingly. 'No I couldn't.'

'Damn it, Larry, we were in the war together.'

LO was eyeing Richardson now. At last he asked, 'Why do you want to know?'

Richardson suppressed a boyish grin and quickly moistened his lips: 'It makes the little hairs stand up . . . on the back of my neck.'

LO grinned back mischievously. 'Well . . .'

Richardson was impatient, could hardly contain himself.

'Sometimes . . .'

Damn it, why was LO taking so long over it? 'Yes . . . ?'

'Sometimes, before bed, she likes to dress up in these old and very delicate lace curtains.'

Richardson repeated the word, a normal, ordinary word after all. 'Curtains . . . ?'

'Beforehand, you see, she's gathered flowers from the garden and arranged them around the room. Their sweetness is overpowering. Each time there's always something different or unusual. Like doves in a cage – or goldfish – or sweetmeats rolled in coconut. Some eccentric trifle that somehow magically completes the scene. On the table by a lantern is a basin of water, with which she bathes me, head to toe. After the bathing, oils are applied, and aromatic tinctures.'

Richardson, now completely transfixed, swallowed drily once or twice.

'Am I boring you?' asked LO.

Richardson shook his square, Northumbrian jowls.

'At last, she stands before me. The lace slips from her shoulders. She has already been anointed. Her skin glows in the soft gold light.'

By now Richardson was gripped in what could only be called an erotic stupor.

'The doves are released, the sweetmeats eaten – slowly, sensuously . . .'

'What about the goldfish?' Richardson asked.

'What. . . ?'

'Doesn't matter, doesn't matter.' Richardson dismissed his question with an impatient gesture of the hand.

'Slowly she moves around the room, floating, gliding, as if on air . . . Until finally, she stops by the lantern and, gesturing to the flowers in their myriad hues, says . . .' With experienced mimicry, LO let his voice fall into cockney vernacular, 'Sixpence a bunch! Sixpence a bunch!'

He was holding up to his friend's face a few flowers he had snatched up from the vase on the table. Richardson, completely nonplussed, gaped back at LO, who still remained as if expecting the next move to come from his friend. Richardson's face was begging the question – 'Is that it?' or 'What now?' – but LO could not contain his deadpan expression any longer and, as Richardson seized the flowers, LO dissolved into uncontrollable laughter.

Richardson's hands tightened on the flowers. His sense of disappointment was monumental. He began to flail LO about the face with the fresh blooms. 'You rotten, wicked sod . . . I never believed a word of it . . . Not a word.'

LO backed away, pleading for mercy. Richardson finally stopped the attack, which allowed LO to gather his wits together, but hardly had he become composed than he dissolved once again into hysterical laughter.

Richardson observed, showing in his tone that he still felt cheated, 'She's too good for you, Larry. Too good by half.'

7

Vivien, animated and vivacious, was up and about again.
Her resilience was quite remarkable, especially when away
from the film set or stage. Her cat, New, a Siamese named
after the New Theatre, and one of Tissy's kittens born in
1944, always played a part in her recuperative process.
They seemed to understand each other so well.

Vivien still had a fragile appearance as she trimmed
away dead leaves from the exotic plants in her greenhouse,
which stood near her own alley of dark cypress trees. New
was twining herself round her, rubbing herself against
her leg. In a red and gold sari Vivien looked stunningly
beautiful. Alone with her cat she would talk aloud to it,
'You *adorable* pussycat. And what have you been doing
lately?' she would say. 'Anything Mummy should know?'

Hearing her voice as he pushed open the wooden-slatted
glass door, LO, knowing his wife's eccentric habits, did
not bat an eyelid.

'That was Korda on the phone,' he addressed her briskly.
'He sends his love and says he's closing down the picture
for two weeks.'

Vivien briefly shut her eyes, and breathed in pleasure.
'Thank God for that . . .'

'He seemed very reasonable. Not at all upset.'

Alexander Korda, Mogul of Elstree, was an exile from
Budapest. All relationships with him were stormy and
tempestuous, not least Vivien's and LO's. Once or twice
in the early days in her career Vivien had slept with him
as a necessary stage in her ascent to fame. She had always

somewhat resented him, not so much for taking advantage of her, but for the failure of *Dark Journey*, the first film they made together, and she feared he never valued her acting highly enough.

Korda used to taunt her that she saw herself as something special, 'Like a Stradivari violin,' he used to tease her, 'too beautiful ever to be played on.' That was it, wasn't it? Kept in a case, exhibited in a museum, or, if played, unwilling to adapt or be interpreted unless the music fitted her shape and sound.

'Why should he be upset?' she demanded imperiously.

LO trod carefully. 'I'm not saying he *should* be.'

'I bet you'd be livid if someone was ill on *your* film.'

He smiled sweetly at her. 'Well, they're not – are they?'

Vivien turned to give New her attention, to show LO she thought her cat the more deserving of her affection. But she was still thinking of Korda. She remembered how firmly he had been against her until he had seen LO and her together. LO's wife, Jill, had been there. It did not matter. Hell, what did it matter? Korda had eyes only for them. He had encouraged their adulterous passion for one another. He was a middle-European voyeur. He wanted to see them making love. He would have filmed them naked, she thought, if he could. She would not have minded either. But LO would have . . .

'How would you like to go to Australia?'

She turned round to face him suddenly. Had he gone completely mad?

'For a year . . . Well almost.'

'Australia?'

'The British Council wants the Old Vic to do a goodwill tour. It shouldn't be too onerous. And there's a cruise at either end.'

'Are you serious?'

'My reaction entirely. Until I thought it over. We could do with the time together, Bibs. And the voyage would do wonders for you.'

But she frowned. New emitted a loud miaow!

'I won't go as your wife. Not as "Lady Olivier".'

'Of course not. We'd lead the company together.'

'I'm not even a member of the company.'

'You leave that to me.' He paused, took a deep breath of the heavy moist air, and grinned. 'So. What do you think?'

'I think . . . I think . . . it would be absolutely perfect.'

This time, instead of New, it was LO who almost began to purr.

'Who else would come?' Vivien asked.

'I'm not sure . . . Mercia and George Relph, perhaps. Peter Cushing, Terence Morgan and his wife, Georgina. Dan Cunningham.'

Vivien almost squealed her delight. She did not notice the warning frown on LO's face.

'What I want is the nucleus for a second company. As a basis for a National Theatre, which the Old Vic will never be. Three plays in repertory on a national tour. I could really weld things together.'

Vivien said, in her fondest and most affectionate tone, thinking how wonderful, perfect, and radiant he was, 'A National Theatre. It's what you've always wanted.'

'It's what this country needs,' he said, as he drew her compliant body to his chest. She came to him willingly. He hardly noticed how weak and soft her body was – devoid of the vibrant tension of her will which gave it its strength.

'Oh Larry,' she was saying. 'To work together again . . . Just like in the beginning. I do love you so. I hate it when we're apart.'

He kissed her.

'It will be good for us Larry. I know it will.'

But already there was a distant look in his eyes, as if he was relishing the triumph. Vivien was gently fondling and kissing his chest. She had a much more personal and intimate dream of what the tour could be like.

8

She felt fulfilled, calmer, steadier, now it was all decided. They had finished *Anna Karenina* without any more attacks of nerves. As LO stayed on at Denham, desperately trying to finish *Hamlet* on time, she could resist the temptation to telephone him in the middle of the night. She had to make do with his letters, which she kept on her bedside table, together with the stack of photographs of him, all signed with endearments. She still idolised him more than she had anyone, even her father, of that she was sure; her infatuation remained intact, like a tent kept from childhood, which when on her own she would bring from the cupboard, peg it down securely, erect it on its poles and climb inside for days on end.

While she stayed down at Notley other sides of her nature tugged at her. Sometimes, as she wandered through the grounds in the deepening twilight, it seemed to her that the silhouettes of the trees were turning into men in evening dress. As the sweet zephyrs from the riverside stirred they became into Scarlett O'Hara's Southern suitors at a ball reaching and bending towards her, imploring her for a dance. LO could send them all packing with his basilisk eye. Yet where was his child, where had it gone? Had there ever been a child of his, growing in her womb? Had it his eyes, his heart, his soul? At what point did a soul enter an unborn child's body?

She pictured the poor creature's popping eyes and shadowy form. She thought of her own daughter, of her first husband, Leigh, and of all that solid, reliable side of life she had abandoned. Could she find it again with LO? Could they not have a child after all? Could it happen in Australia?

But the suitors still beckoned, along the banks of the River Thame. She could never quite renounce their attentions because one day, who knows, she might have need of them again. She might be destitute – left high and dry by LO and in need of rescue.

For the present the Old Vic board had approved that she accompany LO on the tour. Apparently – and she could hardly believe this when LO told her – Tyrone Guthrie had made a special defence of her, calling her England's greatest star. It had been a different story some years before when she had asked him for a job at the Old Vic: he had cold-shouldered her with complete ruthlessness. She wondered just what he might be up to in letting her share the billing with LO as celebrated ambassadors for English Theatre.

Well she would show them she was not a stuck-up outsider, but a solid, hard-working actress, as sound as any of them. Had not all the famous critics of the day praised her to the skies when she played Sabina? The playwright himself, Thornton Wilder, had been most appreciative, although he said her voice was limited. But Larry would help her with her voice, he had promised he could make it stronger and lower. There would be time for that on the tour.

The only problem about going to Australia was that of explaining the situation to New. As she changed for dinner – she always changed for dinner, even if LO was not there, and sat alone at the long, candle-lit dinner table in the solemn refectory – she found the cat in a particularly affectionate mood, and thought that this might be the moment to broach the subject.

Wearing a beige slip whose straps kept sliding from her shoulder, and which otherwise left little to the imagination, she sought the cat's opinion on what dress she ought to wear that evening.

'What about this?' she asked, selecting one from many strewn all over the bed, holding it up against herself to observe the effect in a mirror. 'Too drab?'

She played this game with some four or five dresses, noting that she needed a whole new wardrobe. She seemed in particular to be seeking something to heighten the vamp-like qualities of her face and figure. After a while New grew bored and fell asleep on the double bed. Vivien did not mind this at all.

As she lowered the umpteenth dress over her figure, delighting in the way it revealed to herself the soft moulding of her breasts, she remarked to the cat, 'Oh New, my darling, I'll miss you so. If I told you how much you'd . . .' Here she resisted the temptation to continue with the obvious 'die', and instead said 'cry'.

New reacted by opening her eyes lazily and blinking.

Now she had her audience, Vivien continued, 'But I have to go to sea, you see. To the other side of the world . . . Just me and Larry. Alone. Together. Every day . . . No, you silly, you can't come too. It's upside down. You'd fall right off and simply – float away . . .'

The prospect of this did not seem in any way to affect the cat. But it stimulated Vivien to an even greater effort of communication. Having settled for a quite severely cut green dress with red polka dots which accentuated her slim figure she began to hang the other clothes away.

'Please try and understand,' she pleaded. 'I have to go . . . I do.'

Depositing the dress on the back of the chair by the mirror she approached the cat. Did New not care about her either? She mounted the counterpane and, arching her back, started to crawl seductively over the bed towards her cat. 'I've been so . . . tired and empty . . . Now daddy's going to fill me up and make me just like NEW!' She had hoped the cat might like her game, but it did not take much notice. 'A real cat. A tiger-puss. A naughty, wicked girl.'

She was now on all fours over the cat, legs apart,

stomach and bottom curved above and over the animal in an openly suggestive way. Keeping her girlish, graceful arms still taut, she bent her face down to rub her cheek against the fur. But the cat spat at her and lashed out, scratching the skin of her cheek. She arched back, coiling with fury and almost struck the creature with her hand.

Expecting retribution, now it was New's turn to cower. None came. As the trickle of blood started to run down from the broken skin of her face, Vivien checked herself. Her anger evaporated.

She could concede that she had been in the wrong, and she begged the cat's forgiveness. At the same time her tongue ventured forth from delicious pouting lips, and while she felt mortified by her provocative behaviour, she began to savour the taste of blood on the tip of her tongue.

And so the strange, half-naked figure on the bed, bent over and crouching like a cat, herself put out a soft hand to win back her own pet's affection. She thought of playing Sabina again, and how she fitted the part like an elbow-length glove.

'All that's going to change my darling . . . All that's going to change . . .'

They left England on St Valentine's Day, 14 February 1948. They boarded their train at Euston Station, where they were waved off by all manner and rank of notables. Pictured as the 'perfect lovers' in all the papers, her arm slipped through his, they smiled at the cameras and at each other. The station-master wore a top hat.

At Liverpool their ship, the *Corinthic*, a 15,000-ton refrigerated cargo ship, stood waiting impatiently, churning the water with its propellors. At the dockside Ralph Richardson, Cecil Tennant, the wives and friends of the company had all assembled to see them off on their journey. Vivien, LO and the departing thespians all tossed down streamers from the deck rail. Vivien stood in her long coat of sable black, drinking in the scene of the departure with a huge and satisfied sense of elation. She was as excited as a child and she waved and blew kisses down to Ralph and Cecil on the quayside.

Suddenly her eye caught the form and face of a rough-looking but handsome sailor on the wharf who had a hand raised to her in suggestive greeting – or something more. She could not say what it was about him that affected her, but instinctively she returned the gesture, which made him respond even more fiercely. She caught herself wondering if she knew him and, if so, where had they met? Like the trees at Notley beckoning to her to join them in a dance, he seemed to be summoning her to something more intimate. He also seemed so familiar. Where *had* she seen him before?

She came back to her senses. Suddenly chilled by this momentary aberration, she found herself shivering. LO at the rail next to her, in tune physically with her but completely unaware of what had been going through her mind, put his arm around her to shield her from the cold. She eagerly accepted his protection, nestling in close to his shoulder. But this hardly quelled her alarm at the sight of the sailor.

9

After a cold crossing of the Bay of Biscay they passed
Gibraltar and the entrance to the flat, warm and sunny
Mediterranean. They basked on deck before docking at Las
Palmas in Gran Canaria where numerous British warships,
including an aircraft carrier, stood at anchor. They spent
the day ashore sightseeing, slaking their thirsts with iced
white wine and haggling over big straw hats and other sou-
venirs. Now off the Ivory Coast of West Africa in blazing
sunshine they changed into white flannels and white shorts;
they played housey-housey and deck-tennis, or, affected by
the heat, card-games in the shade of the lifeboats.

'In researching our destination I looked at a number
of books and I've asked Dan Cunningham to read a
"definition" I found in one of them that may or may not
be pertinent. Dan?'

The company were together for the first briefing and LO
had just begun to address them. Cunningham rose from
where he was seated beside Vivien and came to the front
of the assembly. Blond-haired, he had the conventional
handsome looks of a juvenile male lead. He read from the
book LO had handed him:

> The Australian has three main characteristics. An inordi-
> nate love of field sports, a decided dislike for authority,
> and a serious dislike for mental effort of any kind . . .

George and Mercia Relph, seated at the front, laughed
lightly. Of all the company they were the closest friends

of LO and Vivien. Behind them sat the Morgans – Terence had played Laertes in the film version of *Hamlet* – LO had as much as was possible chosen married couples to form the nucleus of his company. Cunningham continued:

He is coarse, strong-jawed, greedy and shrewd, excelling in swimming and horsemanship, but freed from the highest burdens of intellectual development, culture or grace . . . The women, it seems, have very fine legs but little else to recommend them . . .

The others laughed and applauded.

Peter Cushing, a young actor who had played Osric in LO's *Hamlet*, who now arrived late for the meeting, tried to slip in unnoticed.

'Sorry,' he said, 'I thought the afterdeck was before the fo'c'sle.'

Some of the company responded with laughter, but not LO. Neither did Elsie Beyer, the company's general manager, a middle-aged woman who was dressed, still, in a trim suit of tweed. She sat next to LO at the little table in the front of the gathering.

'I will not excuse lateness, Peter,' said LO crisply. 'Don't let it happen again.'

'No, sir,' said the chastened actor. 'I'm sorry.'

'Let me assure all of you,' LO grabbed the opportunity to follow up his reprimand with some more stern words, 'this is no pleasure cruise but a very serious undertaking. Despite the pages just read to you, do not for a moment under-estimate your audience. My instincts tell me they're a whole lot smarter than most stuffy West End matrons. And if they're not, well that's all the more reason for excellence and absolute precision. Elsie will distribute the playscripts now and rehearsals for *The School for Scandal* will commence at once. There'll be a read through in the morning.'

George Relph who had been badly wounded in the throat during the 1914 war, and changed from playing juvenile leads into an accomplished character actor, groaned under his breath, 'And I was just beginning to find my sea legs,' at which Vivien, naughty and rebellious like a schoolchild, laughed out loud.

Elsie turned her attention from LO and, with an officious 'shsssh', silenced her. Submissive though she became, Vivien could hardly believe Elsie could have the gall.

'Breaking in' Vivien was perhaps the hardest task of the outward sea voyage. To some of the company she was strange, to others simply spoiled. On board she had fourteen evening gowns, fourteen afternoon dresses and a large number of hats, shoes and carefully chosen accessories. Yet sometimes, as she told risqué stories in the way a man would tell them, her language unsparing of blushes, listeners would wonder how deep her femininity went, and whether she was not a man masquerading in slim and fragile loveliness. To some younger members, who saw LO and her together for the first time, her personality seemed to smother him completely. God and the Angel they were nicknamed by others.

Vivien quickly fell out with Elsie Beyer, who prompted her so much at one rehearsal of *School for Scandal* that Vivien turned on her, snapping 'One thing at a time please,' then pointedly asked LO if she had the tone right for her part of Lady Teazle.

When LO then said to her, backing up Elsie, 'Yes, but it helps if you get the words right. Let's take it again from the top,' she was frankly amazed, but held back from saying anything until she and LO were alone that night in their stateroom.

'How can you do it in front of that woman?' she stormed at LO furiously.

'Do what? In front of whom?' He seemed genuinely lost.

'That Elsie Beyer.'

'I want you to get it right.'

'You don't have to talk to me like that, do you? It's humiliating.'

'Oh, you'd like special treatment?'

'Yes.'

'I cannot. You're the same as everyone else.'

'I'm your wife.'

'Not during rehearsals.'

Her eyes flashed, but she could not think of an answer to that for the moment.

'Vivien,' he said quietly, with the intention of calming her down. 'If I didn't think you could do it, if I didn't believe in you as an actress, in your potential greatness – I wouldn't bother.'

She had been about to deliver a retaliatory slap to his face, but she now felt humbled and confused.

'What do you mean?' she countered. 'You wouldn't have bothered to marry me?'

LO gritted his teeth at some potential ring of truth about this, but he did not rise to reply to it.

'Darling . . . I went to considerable lengths to convince the board and the company that you should lead this tour. You remember the opposition. Elsie's Old Vic through and through. It's her life. Her vocation. She's totally dedicated. And, as far as she's concerned, you're an outsider – a famous actress, certainly, but an outsider nonetheless.'

'The director's wife?'

'If you like. That's how she sees it.'

'Then to hell with her, Larry, she's just the general manager. Who cares what she thinks?'

'I do – and so should you because she's also the audience. The same as so many more out there. Prejudiced, quite unfairly, but prejudiced nonetheless. And the only way you can turn their heads is with talent.'

She stared back at him uncertainly, but with an appealing look, as if she wanted his support.

'Talent which you have in plenty. If you'll only let me bring it out.'

'What if I have the talent . . . but not the ambition?'

Her piercing, blue-green eyes had recovered some of their old fire, while the delightful turned-up nose was now freckling in the tropical light. These, and the softly sculpted brow with its border of tiny dark hairs springing back from the hairline, the beginnings of glorious curls – all these reflected her passionate and vulnerable nature, and its delicate balance. Could she now trust herself with him?

'Then you'll surely fail.'

What did his words mean? She was unsure.

'I want to be as good as you,' was all she could say.

'You should want to be better.'

'I want to please you, Larry.'

'You should want to please yourself.'

They were talking at cross purposes. She felt desire for him before he felt it for her. She only wanted to climb into that tent, close all the flaps, and have him all to herself.

'I want you to please me . . .'

He turned to say something else but the words died on his lips.

'. . . Please me now.'

Night time was party time aboard the *Corinthic*. The voyage came after eight years of war and stringent restrictions and everyone wanted to let down their hair. They danced and caroused their way down to Cape Town where LO and Vivien had their first taste of being treated like royalty. They had set sail out of Table Bay for Fremantle, but here the *Corinthic* met the infamous Cape Rollers. Elsie observed that if any theatrical management wanted to calm down a company they should put them on the sea between Cape Town and Fremantle. The temperature fell sharply, the ship heaved and rolled, the wind howled terribly.

All this failed to stop the entertaining. It was the Old Vic Company that dominated the proceedings, with the rest of the passengers and crew little more than an appreciative audience.

One night, when they were on the final and more peaceful part of their Indian Ocean crossing – where albatrosses accompanied them – the band played a chord to attract attention, and LO and Vivien emerged into the centre of the empty dance floor to read from scribbled notes. 'Members of the company please to let us know . . .' He paused, then said as an aside to the other passengers, 'This is just for the company actually.'

> . . . When your birthdays are,
> Be they near or far
> So that we may wish you

Vivien took the next three lines:

> All that fate can dish you.
> Otherwise there's no mirth
> In remembrance of your birth,

LO grinned as he completed the stanza, showing the gap between his two front teeth:

> A lonely birthday is no joko
> And we *parentis* are *in loco*!

The audience laughed with delight at their witty duo. The Great Lovers were certainly back in business.

'So tell us please your special date . . .' said LO.

To which Vivien added vampishly, lifting her skirt and rolling her eyes, '. . . Any excuse to celebrate.'

The band struck up a new number, and LO and Vivien led the dancers out on to the floor.

'They're looking chirpy,' Relph observed.

'It's all the exercise they're getting, George,' said Cushing over his shoulder.

'But they're never on deck,' Relph contradicted him.

'Precisely!' said Cushing pointedly.

When a faster number succeeded, and when the dancing had increased in spirit they changed partners. LO danced with Georgina Morgan, Vivien with Dan Cunningham, the latter beginning to flirt openly with her. Elsie stared over at them disapprovingly, while chatting to a ship's officer, who smiled thinly at her efforts to make conversation.

At the end of the number the leader of the band called Viven over to the rostrum and asked if she would take the microphone. She readily agreed and began to sing a moody torch song, which she initially directed towards Cunningham. Everyone began to laugh, although with a discernible edge of embarrassment. But as the pace and momentum of the number increased, she swung her attention unashamedly back to LO who, like a peacock, glowed and expanded in this passionate declaration of love.

At the end of the song, Vivien came over to where he was standing, threw her arms around him and kissed him – desperately – on the mouth.

In her dream the torch song went on and on without stopping. She was no longer on the *Corinthic* but down on the dockside at night. The ground was wet, the air misty. She appeared to be drifting further and further away from the safety of the lights which were located somewhere behind her.

Suddenly in the shadows ahead a figure loomed up. A sailor. The same one who had beckoned to her from the quayside in Liverpool. This time she saw the expression on his face and what his smile revealed when close to: its meaning was brutish and clear.

Vivien stopped. She made a little shake of the head, then shivered slightly. The sailor seized her hand, and she gave way and headed off with him into the swirling mists.

'Vivvy . . . Viv darling,' a voice called from the entrance to the stateroom.

She stirred sleepily. 'What is it?'

'It can't be,' she heard the voice saying a little more distinctly. It was LO. But he was nowhere to be seen.

'Oh darling,' she murmured. 'Promise you'll never leave me. If you do I know I'll . . . die . . .'

'Darling, come outside, quickly.'

She left the bed. She shook her hair. She wore nothing.

Had they made love before going to sleep? She could not remember.

'Hey, Vivvy,' LO said to her by the door, 'you'll catch a cold.'

She reached out for her dressing-gown.

'Can't you smell it?'

'What?'

'Take a breath.'

Tieing the belt of her gown she inhaled deeply. But she could not figure out the smell.

'Gum leaves. Isn't that remarkable?'

'Australia?' she stared out to sea, across the wide expanse of nothing. 'But there's nothing there.'

'Oh, it's there all right.'

Part 2

10

The space was endless, illimitable. The pastures empty. They had hired a tourer and, with the hood pinned back, it swept through the empty land, carrying them from Adelaide to Melbourne. At one point they had driven through miles of great shallow blue lakes with glistening white sand all around; another time ranges of high mountains far away had framed their vision – with some dirty ochre and black cattle in the foreground.

But now with its chromium sparkling their majestic car travelled on a meridian between an ochre sky and an ochre plain. The sun sat behind them, crouching down on the horizon. Far off a flock of pink and grey galahs, disturbed by their passage, rose into the air without a sound.

They had been in Australia a little over a month. In Perth they had arrived at the end of summer, and shaken hands with just about everyone in the city. On their first night they played in an old cinema which had not seen a live show for ten years. The company had sweated in wigs and heavy eighteenth-century costumes in order to charm their audience of two thousand. The audience had been dolled up in their choicest finery: men in top coats and tails or open-necked shirts and summer suits; women, hair piled in high coiffs, draped in daring off-the-shoulder gowns and billowing skirts, decked in every parrot colour imaginable.

They had flown across the Nullarbor Plain to Adelaide where the weather had been cooler, although their reception had been no less tumultuous. One night a hurricane uprooted huge trees in city squares and parks, and swept the roofs off houses. Ships were tossed upon the beaches like corks.

Like fabled lovers in some romance of old, LO and Vivien were mobbed by crowds and garlanded with flowers wherever they went, while throughout their performances clapping and cheering punctuated the lines. When they left Perth, when they left Adelaide, they sang 'Waltzing Matilda' with their audiences. They felt thoroughly spoilt. Now they were alone. At last. The crowds were for tomorrow. LO drove, Vivien sat next to him, feeling the wind in her hair. She turned and smiled at him with her brilliant blue-green eyes, her pretty freckles dancing on her small, tip-tilted nose. She rested her hand on his leg. From some Olympian platform where he had been plotting future ventures he flew down to earth and turned to her. She had been impeccable. He smiled at her as if to say, 'I love you too'.

An hour later he pulled the car to a halt in the dust outside a ramshackle wayside pub; this might be a likely place. Two locals sat drinking on the verandah. LO slammed the car door shut, stretched his arms and yawned. Vivien at once began checking her make-up in the rear-vision mirror. The locals, not bothering to disguise their curiosity, gaped in wonder at the glamorous pair.

LO, feeling constrained to say something to them, called out 'Hello there', to which one of the men nodded a silent acknowledgement, while the other pulled on his drink.

'We're looking,' LO explained, 'for somewhere to stay the night. Does this place offer accommodation?'

Vivien smiled at them, hoping her appeal might tip the balance. Here was a very different Australia from the one that had flocked to their performances, queued all night for tickets, waited on them hand and foot. She was not sure if she liked it; these men were barbarians, cowboys, maybe they would slit your throat as soon as look at you.

The tall thin local, whose ears stood out like animal antennae, gestured with a nod to one side. 'Yer looking at it,' he said.

Her eyes followed LO's and came to rest on a solitary, single-roomed shed. LO turned to her, as if to say 'My God, is that all?' It appeared so terribly basic, as if no one cared. Like the trees out in the bush, their dead limbs splayed out and sprawled everywhere, it was untended, uncultivated. Vivien began to long for the safety of the city.

She went to lay her arm on LO's to ask him if they could drive on. He stuttered politely. 'Uh . . . is it . . . er . . . vacant?'

The spokesman for the locals answered, 'You'd have to ask Harry.'

'The publican? Is he inside?'

'I reckon.'

Wasn't this man peculiar, she thought, weary and aloof, although hardly well off – as tired, as bored, as indifferent as some English aristocrat. She began to feel how unreal the country was.

LO headed off into the pub, leaving Vivien with the two men, who took no notice whatsoever of her. More than this, they seemed so unapproachable. This was a completely new sensation for her.

The second man, who had not spoken to them at all, turned to his companion. 'There was a bloke stayed there Christmas.'

Just as phantom-like, the other man answered. 'Yeah . . . That'd be right.'

For a moment Vivien thought they were addressing her, until it was obvious that she was excluded. She smiled awkwardly. At last they seemed to take in that she was there. A remote kind of interest kindled in them, as if they had noticed a flickering light which had somehow upset their normal expectation.

'From Adelaide, are yer?' asked the one who sucked his beer-can like a young animal its mother's teat.

81

Vivien thought that it was better not to get into any elaborate explanation. 'Yes,' she answered.

'On yer way to Melbourne?'

'That's right.'

'I've got a cousin lives in Melbourne.'

'Oh . . .' She found herself at a loss for words. 'Really?'

She did not of course in any way disbelieve him, but the other man was searching her face for gaps in her credibility. To disarm her he gave a slight nod of verification.

She frowned, trying to match their enigmatic replies with a mystery of her own. They were so familiar, and yet so uncouth. She began to long for the familiarity of the French, the Italians, their pulse was so much nearer to hers than these bleakly honest and open-countenanced cowboys.

Later, at midnight, LO and Vivien were trying to fall asleep in their bare, one-roomed shed which reminded Vivien of a forlorn and empty chicken-shed. But the old weatherboard pub itself was now brightly lit with lanterns and positively throbbed with noise and shouted conversation. Drawn up alongside and behind the building was a remarkable diversity of horse-drawn gigs and gharries, and the occasional petrol-driven conveyance like a truck and a tractor.

LO rose from the bed and opened the door; he wore pyjamas and squatted down on the wooden steps to light a cigarette so as to blow out the smoke and ward off mosquitoes. Behind him, sprawled on her back and twisting uncomfortably as she encountered the lumps and hollows in the sagging three-quarter bed, Vivien was at last dead to the world, a state which always brought LO a feeling of security.

Something in the pub began to engage his attention. He watched as one of the drinkers emerged unsteadily from the hotel. The man walked off the edge of the verandah, missed his step but somehow retained his balance. Weaving a path unsteadily between the horses, shouting at a barking dog to belt up, trying to quieten the shifting restless haunches of the horses awoken to fear by his presence among them – although it was his ill-considered slapping which had sparked their disquiet – he headed across the yard towards LO's and Vivien's sleep-out.

LO jumped to his feet ready to meet the man. But the man walked straight past him, completely oblivious of him, pushing on only to stop in front of a howitzer shell suspended on a chain from the roof. The man picked up an axe handle, leant against the post and started wielding the handle to beat the shell. Behind LO's back, Vivien woke up suddenly, starting up in total disarray.

'Darling, what the hell. . . ?' she called out, jumping from bed to join him by the door where he stood equally bewildered. While prepared to react, he had stayed utterly defeated as to the cause of the alarm. At last the man seemed to have satisfied his need for noise. His urgency gave way to a few desultory blows, then to silence.

LO, adopting the laconic local mode of address, asked, 'Something wrong?'

'Fire alarm,' explained the man.

LO and Vivien looked quickly into the surrounding trees, and then again at the convivial pub lights.

'Where?'

'This is it.'

'Where's the fire?' insisted LO.

'There isn't one.'

Vivien could not help but smile at LO. What had impressed her as inscrutability, was it not just plain dumbness?

'Then why sound the alarm?'

'Harry told me.'

'The publican,' explained LO to Vivien, although this did not make the man's behaviour any clearer.

'Why?'

'To see if it works.'

LO's face began to crease, for the humorous aspect of the situation could no longer be contained. Vivien just looked utterly amazed.

'G'night,' said the alarmist, repeating his journey through dog and horses.

But the humour of their first encounter with the Australian hinterland quickly wore off. They could not wait to escape. They turned to gather up their belongings and leave. The emptiness all around was waiting for them, with the foliage of the trees so dark, like black iron-work. Perhaps the locals seeing them in the chrome-plated roadster thought they were government inspectors, come to check on their readiness to fight bush fires.

As LO drove on into the night, he and Vivien could see more cause for such a strange rite. Hundreds of dead trees stood either side of the road, their limbs partly charred by fire. But it was an illusion – or, high above the tall trunks, were there mops and clusters of sprouting growth which a full moon endowed with an exaggerated ripeness? What a strange land, Vivien reflected.

Later, driving in the open bush again, they stopped beside the road in what seemed like a clearing. They lit a fire and happily guzzled local red wine straight from the bottle. LO had his heavy camel-hair overcoat draped over his shoulders, while Vivien was wrapped in a rug. The car now had its hood down.

'I love it here,' Vivien said to him. 'It's so wild and empty. This was what it must have been like at the beginning of time.'

LO was engaged in reading the lengthy message inscribed on the label of the wine bottle. 'How can they make such damn good wine and run such rotten pubs?'

'It's the same everywhere. Rundown hotels. Airless rooms. Casual service.'

'But the succulent lamb chops they give you. Huge steaks with eggs on them. Oysters. Fresh milk and butter. Lashings of beer.'

'Some of the boys were crying at the grub in Adelaide. They'd never seen anything like it.'

'We swopped food for tales of hardship in England,' said LO.

'Why did we bring our theatre here?' asked Vivien.

'To civilise the natives,' replied LO with a grin.

'How impertinent . . .' she mused, while the tiny elusive dimple at the edge of her chin deepened. 'Like taking burlesque to paradise.'

LO was appalled and threw up his hands. 'Shakespeare! You call it burlesque?'

'He wrote it for the common folk.'

'These people aren't common. They're prehistoric!' His expression grew more serious. 'It'll be different in Melbourne and Sydney.'

'This country,' said Vivien. 'It's still a secret. Like us.'

'You're pissed,' said LO.

'Nobody knows us, Larry. They only know what they see.'

'Oh do they . . .'

'Nobody knows what we're really like. Not even us.'

He turned his head quizzically and a frown line appeared. 'You are pissed.'

She took no notice. She looked up at the stars, the Milky Way, no longer a brilliant path directly overhead, but over to one side of the sky, towards what seemed to be the south. Even so, a great sense of unity and strength came over her. Tonight was the night when they could try again, if she had counted the days accurately . . .

'I do so much want us to have a baby.'

'Vivien don't . . .' LO admonished her in a gentle tone, from which she took no suggestion of warning or protection. She felt so clear, so sure, it would all be possible. 'Don't do this to yourself.'

'I've had one, I can have another.'

'We've tried, Viv. Twice. Could you face it again?'

'Yes. I have to. We both do. We must.'

'Vivien . . .'

'Larry, I left my child . . .' She could not, for a moment,

85

go on. When she did it was with less pain. 'And you left yours. We need to make things better.'

'I thought you wanted to act.'

'I do. I want to act and I want your child. I want everything.'

He leaned towards her, and he was smiling sympathetically. She reached for the wine bottle, but he pulled it away.

'No . . . There's not enough.' But he relented and handed it over. She closed her hand round it, examined it, turned it upside down and let the rest of the contents gurgle away into the sand.

'What are you doing?'

'Making a libation. To us. To a baby . . .'

'I was enjoying that wine . . .'

She turned to face him. 'Make love to me, Larry.'

'What? Here? In the *outback*.' He comically emphasised the word in a very English manner.

'Before I die,' she said passionately.

'You're crazy. You know that, don't you?'

'Isn't that why you love me?'

He smiled and nodded gently. Indeed, it was probably part of the attraction. He caught her by the shoulders, changing position to kiss her. She moved away and spread the rug which had enveloped her. He pulled his coat over them both as they lay down, tenderly seeking out one another's mouths. She was at first almost shy and felt oddly vulnerable, there under the southern sky, under an open sky with the air all open around her. She clung to him tightly and willed him as she gave herself entirely to him to make her a child.

11

'Hell's black intelligencer' was putting the finishing touches to his make-up in the dressing-room backstage at the Princes Theatre Melbourne. LO had now entirely vanished into his impersonation of Shakespeare's sexually attractive but disgraceful Richard III. The massive concentration of nose putty was the main feature of the disguise, an almost obscene protuberance built out of the centre of the face. It made LO look about as unlike LO as possible. Together with the harness of his hump, now buckled into place and his cod-piece, which also enlarged reality to an almost absurd degree, LO was ready to work his audience to a pitch of dramatic excitement as had 'rarely been experienced in the theatre'.

Out in the front of house, before the audience's noisy expectation had finally settled into the silence of the curtain rising, a young man stood in a stall aisle, persuading the usherette that, in order to be able to watch the performance, he did not need anything so mundane as a ticket.

Only a year or so older than thirty, the man was wiry and thin, with black wavy hair and a roguish, almost insolent expression on his face.

'It's all right, darls,' he was saying. 'I don't have a ticket. I'll just stand here with you.'

The usherette was about to send him packing when she recognised him as Peter Finch, the Australian actor.

'Why, Mr Finch. What are you doing here?' Her eye spotted the house manager bearing down on her. 'Look, I'd love to but I can't. It's more than my job's worth.'

The lights in the auditorium began to dim. Finch raised his finger to his lips. 'Shssh . . . He's on.'

Advancing as the black toad of Shakespeare's invention, down tunnels and corridors that led to the wings of the theatre, LO saw stage-hands waver, step aside quickly, or even turn back. Instinctively they wanted to give him a wide berth. He loved the character now with his naked and unashamed lust for power. His own mind prior to going on was at one with the shallow rapid pace of the character. The quickness, energy, violence, unexpectedness, they were all there, ready to switch on at a touch of the button. Inside him energy simmered and bubbled, ready to explode. Reaching the iron ladder by the prompt corner of the theatre, by means of which the lighting man climbed to his board, LO seized hold of it, a hand on either side, and shook the frame with all his might till it rattled and screamed – gearing up his strength for the performance.

Next day, towards noon, LO was back at work in the theatre, rehearsing. Although the reviews for the first night in Melbourne had been mostly good, there were one or two features of the production he felt could be improved. He was not convinced that he had conquered the acoustics of the place as well, and now, in dark suit and grey tie, he capered with flamboyant theatrical gestures upon the empty stalls while declaiming:

Da de da de da de da
De da de da de da!

Reaching the footlights, he grimaced out front with murderous glee, quite unaware that Elsie Beyer was sitting in the stalls with piles of administrative clobber on her knee, trying to sort out the chaos that arrival in a new city entailed. The stage director, David Kentish, who had worked all night before the opening, stood on stage in attendance to LO in front of the green backcloth with its quintessential English fields – small, enclosed with fences – its castle and battlements.

LO moved quickly backwards and, in three quick leaps, swung himself up towards the mezzanine cloisters. He stopped short of completing his action, reaching out for a handhold on a column beyond his grasp.

'You see,' he said. 'It's far too far away. It ruins the entire movement.'

'But it's balanced by the column on the other side. The main problem is the stage. It's far too big.'

'Who are we designing the set for, David? The theatre or the performance? I want it moved . . .' LO then added somewhat cynically, '. . . and the other one too, if symmetry's so important.'

At that moment Peter Cushing appeared on the stage, he too was dressed in street clothes.

'Ah, Clarence . . . Let's take a look at scene four,' said LO. 'I've got a new idea.'

At the back of the stalls there was a slight commotion and a brief exposure to the wilder light of day. Through the open door walked the elegantly dressed Antonia Vaughan, accompanied by a sharply suited member of the press corps who carried a flash camera. Antonia, the drama critic of one of Australia's largest selling women's magazines, came from Sydney where she was prominent in artistic circles.

She waited for her eyes to adjust to the gloom and then sauntered down the aisle towards the stage. Elsie, her watchdog instincts roused, let her papers slip to the floor, then crossed to meet these invaders. Very conscious of the need to preserve the silent intimacy of LO's rehearsal she spoke in a hushed tone to counter the brash manner of the journalist. Antonia deflected Elsie's attempts to usher them out by pointing out haughtily that her request for an interview had been approved, and that she had spoken with LO himself the day before. As Elsie had no means of checking the truth of this without disrupting the rehearsal, she let the couple remain in the auditorium.

Antonia and her photographer slipped down into a pair

of seats, where the critic was content to watch, fascinated by the rare privilege of seeing a great actor in rehearsal. For the cameraman, the temptation was irresistible. Unnoticed by Elsie, he raised the camera to his eye.

LO was stopped in mid-sentence by the flash.

'Good God, what was that?' He strode forward to the edge of the stage to peer out into the gloom. 'Oh . . . The press!'

Antonia looked daggers at her companion and apologised weakly.

LO scowled, spitting out his venom with considerable theatrical volume. 'Give 'em an inch, they take your bloody soul! Ah –'

The spontaneous reaction had provoked something worse, and LO let out a gasp of pain as his hand shot out to hold his right leg above the knee. It was the old knee pain again, echo of an ancient injury.

Antonia was aware that this was not a very auspicious beginning.

'I apologise Miss Vaughan, but my mood could be better.'

They were both in his dressing-room. LO had a towel around his neck and moved gingerly about the room to stop the leg stiffening up.

Antonia Vaughan noticed the folded paper on the dressing-table.

'Yes,' she answered. 'I read the review.'

'Of course that doesn't bother me . . .' he said, although it was all too clear that it bothered him a great deal. 'I hurt my knee on stage. It's got nothing to do with the critics.'

He picked up the review and scanned it again.

'This has to be the most piss-elegant, nervously smug city I've ever played in.'

The coldness of the first night audience had surprised him. Row upon row of 'boiled shirts' – they had sat in absolute silence, unified in high, perhaps exaggerated expectation. He much preferred the easy-going style of

Perth. The boys in the company found Melbourne a dreary place, shabby and rather dingy in the aftermath of wartime austerity. They had eight weeks there to stick out.

He read aloud from the paper: 'We have better Richard IIIs here in Melbourne . . .' He pulled with thumb and finger at his ear. 'Well I'd like to see them. It's never too late to learn. Do you know this critic?' He fixed his gaze upon the blue-eyed woman who seemed to him as if she knew her way about.

'Well, not as a critic . . . He's their Parliamentary roundsman.'

'Then my sympathies are with the politicians.'

LO's nervous eyes kept scanning the review again and again. 'At least Vivien gets a good notice . . . She's been working so terribly hard.' Then as if speaking to himself, and with genuine enthusiasm he observed, 'I think it's the best thing she's done.'

This provoked an unexpectedly cheeky reply from Antonia. 'Not that you're competitive?' she said.

The sally threw him off balance. Women in England did not reply like that, they had not been granted the licence by men. Unless, of course, they were Vivien. Antonia gave him a strange, exposed smile. There was nothing coarse in either her expression or about her outspokenness. He could not justifiably take offence, so he contented himself with answering, in a deadpan tone, 'Who on earth told you so?'

She smiled. Still the strange, exposed smile.

'*Are* there better Richard IIIs in Melbourne?'

She replied in a slow, lilting tone, somewhat tickled that he could show such insecurity. 'Anything's possible in a random universe . . .'

'You're not taking me seriously.'

'I just don't want you to take that review seriously.'

He liked people to stand up to him. She had no desire to flatter her way into having influence over him – like so many English women. Maybe men and women were more equal in Australia.

'And is your newspaper more discerning, Miss Vaughan?'

'It's not a newspaper. It's a magazine.'

'Oh . . . A *pictorial*.'

The duel was amusing him. It was genial, but conducted with a kind of watchful will. He found it refreshing how Australians would, in talking, put so much of themselves to one side. They were really much more aware than he had at first realised. They watched you, put some of themselves aside, failed to take account of what they were and what they did, and watched you to see if you would do the same. It was a variation on the old English habit of understatement – which recently had all too easily deteriorated into a blundering and foolish lack of self-respect.

'With no bent for critical analysis, I'm afraid. We're more interested in what you make of Australia than what Australians make of you.'

'How refreshing . . .' said LO, failing to see that she was leading him into a trap.

'And what do you make of Australia, Sir Laurence?'

Was she paying homage to him, or sending him up? He was not too sure, and again her blunt invitation to comment threw him off balance.

'Hmm . . .' he blustered, but quickly recovered the old English trick of insincerity, made easier for him by his tendency to act all the time. 'Oh charming, utterly charming . . .' He waved the paper at her. 'I find your openness and honesty quite beguiling.'

Delicately, but clearly intending to ram the point home, he dropped the paper into the waste basket and fixed her with a hollow smile. Then the pain came on once more, and he limped away from the basket.

Alert with all her instincts she asked him, 'Are you all right?'

'It's the limp I employ as Richard. The game leg gets the glory – and the straight one gets the pain!' He grinned boyishly.

'Is it serious?'

'It comes and goes. A minor irritation.'

'You mean like reporters?'

She had a grasp, too, of theatrical innuendo. Maybe, after all, there *were* better Richard IIIs in Melbourne. He kept his studied politeness, but what he now said to her offered many different possibilities of interpretation.

'Oh, I wouldn't say that, Miss Vaughan . . .'

12

She was disappointed again. She could feel her period about to come on in three or four days' time. Like the sea breaking on the shore, the tide of her monthly cycle was sweeping over the sandcastle of hope they had built when they made love in the outback.

She felt like she always felt before her period: on edge, quick to take offence, hysterically critical of everyone, especially LO.

What did he care if they had a baby or not? He had his Richard and he had his knighthood. He was dangerous – *and* respectable. They lived in a safe, exhausted time, and everyone wanted to identify with a dull, safe and married couple. Think of the future, my dear, and save, save, save . . .

In front of the cameras they gazed at one another with misty eyes, praised one another in just the right tone of adoration. It had all begun to nauseate her.

She had much preferred the war years when people had seen her and LO as Lady Hamilton and Nelson, or him as Heathcliff and her as Scarlett O'Hara; when press and public had condoned their adultery to keep the passion simmering. She was so much more excited by the idea of threatening the husbands of this world, instead of gratifying them and making them feel safe – safe to go off and betray their wives, or earn fortunes to keep them enslaved at home. The harmless form of treachery the world loved – the romance of adultery – gave her energy. It fed the ordinary man and woman's imagination with hope of change, with hope of escape. It was the very fabric of which dreams were made . . .

Now hope was destroyed. As Lady Anne she was acting with LO in *Richard III*. Nightly she made of herself a piteous spectacle of reluctant, then unrewarded love, while he cavorted round her, enjoying his naked lustfulness.

Richard:	Say, then, my peace is made.
Anne:	That shalt thou know hereafter.
Richard:	But shall I live in hope?
Anne:	All men, I hope, live so.
Richard:	Vouchsafe to wear this ring.
Anne:	To take is not to give.

Once upon a time, before the knighthood, she would look forward to the interval. LO would lock his dressing-room door and there would be champagne and oysters, sometimes even time for a quick consummation devoutly to be wished . . . Now he would just call in his secretary and dictate letters – without even removing his lank black wig or bloody boots.

She was beginning to find his performance as Richard obscene. Maybe she was just identifying – or over-identifying – with Lady Anne. But she felt Richard taking him over more and more. He now had to be first in every race. Playing Richard revised and reinforced an inner heartlessness. The performance of naked power gave him the electric delight which she could no longer provide. Did LO love Richard too much?

She wore a pale lime-green dress and a blood-red rose at her waist. She was pressing the cork upwards on a bottle of champagne. She was in a party mood, thank God. Being a Scorpio, so an old crone had once told her, parties gave licence to her extremity of nature. Scorpios were said to eat themselves up, to burn themselves out.

She was about to thrust the bottle between her legs

without ceremony when the cork plopped and took flight towards the exquisite Victorian ceiling of the Princes' circle bar. The scene was so English she could imagine she was in Oxford.

'Wheee . . . Roaring to go!' she cried. 'Here we are, Miss Vaughan, a live one.'

She pressed a glass of spitting champagne into Antonia's hand.

'Thank you, Miss Leigh.'

'You really must call me Vivien.'

Antonia nodded in appreciation. 'I'm Antonia.'

'Cheers, Antonia. How did you manage to warm Larry up? You're the first member of the press who's been allowed into the inner sanctum.'

'Really? I'm honoured.'

'Yes, Larry usually takes to journalists with an axe.'

'Well, he did nick me on initial contact.'

Vivien raised an eyebrow. This intrigued her. 'How did you avoid serious injury?'

The wide-eyed innocence in her tone concealed a deadly intent. But Antonia was on her guard.

'I just threw myself on his mercy, basically.'

Her watchful eyes kept Vivien at arm's length. Both were beautiful women whose talk matched their looks, so that everyone at the party watched them. Vivien spied in particular Elsie Beyer's eyes glued to her. But in spite of the Christian name familiarity neither could be truly frank. Nor could Antonia resist paying homage to Vivien.

'He does like that.'

'He's just kind to older ladies.'

Vivien stiffened. This was an idea definitely alien to her, broad and threatening. Womanhood. Motherhood, in particular. Growing up, moving forward.

She forced a smile, gave out bold signals to the effect that she could not see how Antonia had got round LO.

'Well, I think us *older* ladies' – Vivien emphasised the word – 'should beware of Sir Laurence this evening. Our ageing knight has obviously done his good deed for the day.'

Antonia said nothing.

A sense of unreality hovered over Vivien for an instant. She retrieved the half-empty bottle, refilled their glasses, and downed the contents of her own thirstily.

'It's French,' she chattered on. 'I can't abide your Australian bubbly. You don't mind me saying that?'

Antonia had stayed strangely mute. Vivien had rejected her warm side, her mothering side, and now the journalist seemed remote and absent, an alien from another world whom she could patronise with English social chat.

'Of course not.'

Even Antonia could behave like a puppet and answer on cue.

'I love your ports and sherries, but your other wine, ugh.'

'Just don't criticise our beer . . . or our men.'

'I adore your beer. But I can't offer an opinion on your men yet I'm afraid. Still, there's six months to go.'

Antonia raised her glass, as if to salute Vivien's touching on another side of life, one she knew about, and over which they might make contact. She could also see that Vivien was drinking heavily. Was it that she just loved chit-chat, as some women did?

'Here's hoping.'

Vivien laughed excessively, gulped more champagne, relishing the hot, free and easy mood that was upon her. Her instinct had been right – Antonia *was* a man-eater. 'Everyone is so in awe of Laurence, they treat me like bone china.'

She was thinking the opposite. Out in the Melbourne streets on a walk that afternoon, Vivien had noticed how everything was so out of control. She had caught a crowded tram, been jostled, pushed against the big-boned men and women. The men had eyed her, gaping.

She adopted a mocking tone. 'Not one Australian man has even made a pass at me.'

'Count yourself lucky,' said Antonia.

'You're not under any illusions about Englishmen, I hope. The upper classes are remote and in decay, the middle classes narrow-minded and petty, while the rest are strictly beyond the pale.'

'What does that say for your husband?'

'Oh, Larry is not what he seems . . . Thank God.' Suddenly she remembered Antonia was a journalist. 'But I'm telling you too much.'

'Please, my readership wants fairy tales, I won't be writing this.'

'You're not enamoured of your profession, are you?'

'Is any journalist over forty?'

'You Australians are forthright.'

'So are you.'

'Perhaps . . . but I wouldn't admit to anything over thirty-one . . .'

LO was chatting much more soberly with the younger men of the company, who, while listening respectfully, were eyeing one or two delectable Melbourne girls – built so differently from their skinny and underfed counterparts in London. These tall, long-limbed girls had amazing breasts and legs. Even so, the boys knew there could be no fast living with them. Only decent and demure relations were permitted – restricted to dances and taking the girls home in taxis; picnic lunches and grand receptions; tennis parties and bathing parties; outings in motor launches from the yacht club.

'Clarence thinks it's a mistake,' LO was explaining. 'His first line is a joke.'

'But that doesn't mesh with the rest of the scene,' Peter Cushing answered. 'Clarence is obviously terribly worried . . .'

'But we need a contrast to the tone of my soliloquy – we need something light . . .'

LO turned away from the direction of Elsie Beyer, who he knew was watching him, possessive and protective as ever, to find himself facing Vivien. She had brought Antonia over.

'For Heaven's sake, Larry. Don't you ever stop.'

'It was a wonderful performance,' Antonia said quickly to LO, giving him no chance to react to Vivien.

Antonia turned to the rest of the company. 'Congratulations . . .' She made a gesture to include them all, not omitting Vivien. 'Everyone . . .'

'You're too kind,' said LO blinking his eyes – or suffering them to twitch involuntarily.

Vivien stabbed him with her knee and said, in an audible aside, 'Well, of course she is. She's being polite . . . For God's sake, don't take it to heart . . .'

'But I loved it, really,' insisted Antonia.

'God, this party's boring . . .'

Just at this moment Dan Cunningham crested the top of the staircase: the quintessential, blond, baby-faced Englishman with a boarding-school background, he seemed suddenly to offer Vivien salvation. Here was Cherubino . . .

She took Antonia's hand. 'In the nick of time. Come on, Antonia. Dan has volunteered to be the life and soul of the party.' She appealed to Cunningham. 'Haven't you, precious?'

'Hello . . . Who's this?' said Cunningham stuffily.

'Antonia's a reporter, Dan. She can get you headlines.'

'What do I have to do?' Dan scratched his head in mock bewilderment.

'Say something scandalous – about Australian women.'

'But I like Australian women . . .'

'That's not scandalous. That's flirting. That won't get you anywhere.'

'Yes, it could.'

They all laughed wickedly.

'Come on, you two,' Vivien called out to Georgina and Terence Morgan. 'Join the fun. Find another bottle . . .' And she poured champagne for everyone, now completely abandoned to her manic, party-going mood. Antonia glanced back at LO, wondering what he might be thinking, not really expecting to catch his eye. But he managed a faint smile and toasted her with his glass. His mask was wearing thin.

13

This was by no means the first of the Old Vic's noisy sessions into the early hours. In Perth and Adelaide the parties had not attracted much attention. But here in Melbourne – the holy city as it was called because of the great number of Anglo-Saxon places of worship which dominated the sky-line – tongues were beginning to wag.

Elsie, too, had become increasingly subject to the strain of her self-appointed task of guardian to 'God' and 'The Angel'. It was one thing to protect them from too much pressure from outside – and ensure clear passage for them from stage door to taxi, calling like a major domo, 'Make way for Sir Laurence and Lady Olivier.' It was quite another to try and intercede between them and their worst selves.

'And some are still in the bar at two or three in the morning,' she was complaining to the Old Vic's leader next morning. LO himself was looking rather the worse for wear.

'Elsie . . .' he began with a mixture of kindness and warning.

'Sir Laurence,' she interrupted, taking a deep breath. 'It needs to be said. Your wife is the worst offender. If not the ring leader.'

LO's mood quickly changed. 'That's not your concern . . .' he said frostily, eyeing the poor spinster's old-fashioned hairdo which she had in vain, the day before, tried to have improved.

'I *am* the general manager . . .'

'And *I'm* the artistic director,' LO retaliated swiftly. 'When it starts to affect performances, well, then I'll do something about it. For pity's sake, Elsie, these people aren't children!'

He then felt he had been rather unkind, especially as Elsie had so often been trundled out before the press as a substitute for himself and Vivien. Dubbed the Old Vic 'Mother', Elsie would prattle on about him and 'Lady Olivier' as being two of the kindliest, friendliest people you could ever meet.

'They're just trying to wind down, Elsie,' he pursued the same line in a kinder tone. 'After eight performances a week in a gruelling season with precious few breaks. Don't you see your attitude brings its own tensions?'

Now it was her turn to be offended. She had just been feeling depressed and had declared in a letter to a friend at home, 'The whole of Melbourne seemed to close in on one and no matter how you hacked away at the work, you just couldn't get through.'

'My *attitude*?' she coughed and spluttered.

LO quoted her back at herself. ' "It needs to be said," Elsie, there have been complaints.'

He was not just making this up. Vivien, who had complained Elsie treated her like a child and had brought others to the point of desperation, was all for sending her home. They had discussed the possibility with the representative of the British Council. But LO had remained too soft-hearted to give her the outright sack.

Incensed, Elsie asked, 'From whom?'

LO back-pedalled, adopted a hurt, piggy-in-the-middle tone to win himself some sympathy. 'You complain about her Elsie, and she complains about you. Is that so surprising?' He made a dismissive gesture. 'Now, can we get on with matters at hand?'

Shoved to one side as she now felt, she had to obey the boss. She addressed herself to the papers on her desk.

'There's seven . . . no eight requests for you to speak at various functions, including one from the British Empire League.' She would make sure she had her way here, if nowhere else, by making sure LO put on a good show. 'The city council has arranged a reception and so has the yacht club – at least they've offered a cruise – and they'd like Madam,' – she stopped a moment on the word and looked at him for signs of concession – 'to launch a new boat.'

'Is that all?'

'Unless you want to answer these.'

She held up a wire basket of fan mail – about six hundred letters – as if it was an ultimate weapon, for she knew how he insisted on answering every letter ever written to him.

He swallowed heavily. 'How many are there?'

'About two hundred a day at the moment. Should be a thousand by the end of the week.'

His attention was deflected by the sight, through the glass panel of their wall, of a young woman who had wandered into the upstairs foyer looking lost.

'Anything else?' he asked distractedly, his eyes following the blurred form.

'Well you'll have to decide which of these functions you're attending. They'll all want you to make a speech.'

'It *is* a goodwill tour, Elsie. I don't like to disappoint them . . .'

Elsie sighed. That meant he would go to them all. Would he never learn?

The young woman had now found their office and was knocking at the open door.

'Excuse me . . .' she said round the door.

LO rose and straightened his tie. 'Ah you must be –'

'June Kelly.'

He looked distressed at Elsie's presence. Elsie drew herself up to her full height.

'It's a pleasure to meet you, Sir Laurence,' said Miss Kelly.

'Ah quite . . . This is our general manager, Elsie Beyer.'

'Hello,' said the girl brightly.

Elsie stared at June over the top of her spectacles – the lenses would change according to her mood and they were now very dark – and then looked back at LO as if to question the identity of this intruder.

LO shifted awkwardly, scratched his cheek. 'I thought I might get someone to help with the correspondence . . .'

Elsie cocked her head haughtily. This was her job, let no one forget it. She felt all the power that resided in the six hundred letters draining away.

'*Personal* correspondence of course . . . Nothing to do with the company.'

'There's nothing to spare in the budget,' she retorted.

'Yes, yes I know. Now unless there's something else . . .?' LO had upstaged her, no longer prepared to think about it further.

Forced to collect her papers, she gathered them up from the desk and prepared to leave, salvaging what shreds of dignity she could. She gave June a withering look, but the girl again flashed her a winning smile.

As soon as she was alone with LO, June brought some letters out of her bag. 'I've got some references if you'd like to see them?'

'Can you type?' LO sat without moving.

It was June's turn to be thrown: the question was so obvious.

'Yes.'

'Quickly?'

'Yes.'

LO extended his hand. 'Welcome aboard.'

This time she smiled vivaciously at him. He seized the basket of fan mail.

'Now first things first,' he said in a tone of sudden weariness. He upended the basket on to the desk so that

104

the correspondence spilled out and formed a huge pile. 'What on earth do we do with these?'

She picked up a letter at random and scrutinised the handwriting before tossing it back on the desk.

'I could make a suggestion . . .'

LO relaxed, and gave his new personal secretary a big grin.

14

As part of their mission of being a goodwill tour, the Old Vic Company often behaved as ambassadors, thanking the Australians – as LO did on numerous occasions – for taking part in the Allied war effort. They also gave talks on the acting profession and in the process stirred the ambitions of the young. As a leader in a Melbourne paper remarked, 'There can be no doubt that the Old Vic season has had an immense influence on the theatre-going public here; it has given thousands of people a taste for the legitimate stage.'

Some local performances seen by members of the company resulted in actors being signed up to come to England – the Old Vic School was keen to cream off the best of English-speaking talent. Other local talent felt desperate to be spotted, but was not – or did not quite know how to go about it.

Peter Finch had become fascinated – indeed obsessed – by LO's style of acting, and was in a mood to do anything to meet his hero. Finch was performing in the suburbs, 'taking' classics to the workers. He and the company he had formed were acting in a travelling version of Molière's *The Imaginary Invalid* – the production abridged to less than fifty minutes.

Finch was extremely ambitious. Weary of touring in dead-end holes, he wanted to spread his wings. He had an arrogant confidence that he had something different to offer, a new and honest style of acting, a take-me-as-I-am directness – the kind of quality the old world might soon be looking for in the new.

Finch arranged through Antonia Vaughan, who was a girlfriend of his, for Vivien and LO to see his Molière. He and Antonia had an intermittent, casual relationship, with the mutual exchange of favours, including those of a sexual variety. They could take from one another, receive from one another, but need not in any way become close. They were free from enquiry – or even knowledge about one another. They could exploit, respect, and leave each other alone.

Finch's acting was daring, quirky, aggressively real. As the performance took place at lunch time, LO and Vivien, flattered and cajoled into attendance by Antonia, could fit it in their busy schedule. The hall was in fact a factory canteen, and the premier knight of the English stage relished his submergence among sandwich-munching, tea-swilling ordinary Aussie workers.

Finch, as Argan, played in costume. Tall, periwigged, he worked in a disarming, insolent way, conjuring up completely unexpected effects. LO at once recognised the young actor's potential and insisted that he, Antonia, and Vivien meet Finch after the performance.

They found him in the factory washroom, removing his make-up at a splashed and peeling mirror.

'The style was so perfect for the material,' LO commented generously. To which Vivien added, 'So fresh and simple . . .'

Finch accepted their compliments with a smile and simple nod of the head. Vivien was at once strangely moved and affected by this young man, so good, so clever at his work, yet so completely unknown in the world at large. He seemed the very antithesis of all that she and LO stood for. She had noticed in the tights he wore long powerful legs – a swimmer's, a surfer's legs – but now she could recognise in his long and lean face, so much at odds with the be-rouged visage he showed under the wig, much more of the ironical stoicism, the devil-may-care nonchalance, of other Australian men.

'I'd love to claim it's original,' he said of his acting. 'But I can't. It was basically how the *commedia dell'arte* did Molière.'

'I was going to say it reminded me very much of Rossi's productions –' LO began.

'I worked with Rossi,' Finch interrupted.

'Really! In Rome?'

'No, Libya.'

'Libya!'

'Yes, he was taken prisoner at Tobruk. I used to put on shows for the Italian POWs. He helped me stage them.'

'Good God!'

While the two men chatted, Vivien hungrily watched Finch, who was unselfconsciously removing his doublet, revealing a well-muscled, trim, hard torso. She did not notice that Antonia carefully watched for the effect Finch would have on her, the older woman remembering their spirited exchange at the party about the Australian male.

Some of this Antipodean handsomeness rubbed off on LO, too, who drew energy from Finch's brashness, his apparent innocence.

'And whose idea was it to tour factories like this?'

'Mine, I think,' said the younger man cockily.

Several workers passed through the changing room to use the urinal next door. Vivien noticed how little affected by the presence of the 'quality' they were, vulgarly stretching, fixing their trousers as they emerged. They were not down-trodden in manner so you never had to feel that you were patronising them, speaking down to them – somehow taking their part – as you had to with the English working man. They had the air of owning every place where they stood. 'It's a free country', they seemed to proclaim with every look they gave you.

'Bloody good stuff, mate,' said one, who accosted Finch on his way out.

To address the man Finch hardly lifted his voice – and certainly did not change his style of address. 'Glad you enjoyed it.'

'What was it called again?'

'*The Imaginary Invalid.*'

'Pommy one was it?'

'French as a matter of fact.'

'Go on, don't normally understand foreign lingo that well.'

Vivien could now recognise this as not just bloody-minded ignorance – but as Australian humour. She looked over at Antonia, who smiled at the hardcase exchange. It was a measure of understanding this form of drollery that you never sought to correct or cap it. It acted in conversation like a punch line in reverse – a 'de-punch' line.

'It's all in the acting, mate,' said Finch.

The man strolled off, shaking his head. 'Good on ya, digger. Funny! Fair choked me.'

LO regarded this like an avid newshound, keen not to miss any reaction. No doubt, thought Vivien, he had stored away every small item of vocabulary, to use at a later date.

Afterwards they ate lunch in an old greasy-spoon Chinese restaurant, where the habitués sat at scrubbed wooden tables. There was none of that 'ethnic food' sophistication so widespread forty years later in Australian cities. The wallpaper looked dirty, flypaper hung from a plastic lampshade in the middle of the room, while an old Chinese woman with gold in her few remaining teeth, flip-flopped backwards and forwards with plates of *dim sung*, Peking prawn, steaming scallop and crab in garlic.

The dingy atmosphere, with its family warmth and intimacy, reminded Viv of her school holidays in India, when Daddy would journey with her from their hill station where he bred horses down into the local town, leaving Mummy behind at home, where she would count her rosary beads, watchful and suspicious that he was leading his daughter astray.

Of course he was doing no such thing: just enjoying an innocent flirt with his daughter, swopping his slightly risqué jokes – which gave her an unsatisfied longing for real dirt – with her schoolgirl stories, and feeding her up with the local delicacies.

'Perhaps there *are* better Richard IIIs in Melbourne,' she heard LO saying. Could he never give up thinking or talking about the theatre? Could he never believe there was a life outside? When was the last time he had read a novel? She believed that he had only ever read two novels in his whole life – *Wuthering Heights*, which he always told reporters was his favourite, and *Gone with the Wind*, which he had read so that he could coach her for the screen test.

'You mean,' Antonia smiled wryly at Vivien as she drew on her cigarette, 'down at the dockyards during "smoko".'

Vivien laughed.

'Really, I admire what Peter's doing, I do,' LO went on. 'It goes right back to the beginnings of theatre. Like Shakespeare's matinées at the Globe. And to find it here in Australia!'

Really, his Anglican vicar's son tone of condescension sometimes made her boil. That inevitable sense of hierarchy and 'the form'. To find something cultured or polished in the colonies – as unusual, my dear, as finding a natural actor in the Gorbals. Vivien reflected bitterly that all actors of LO's generation were, without exception, upper or middle-class – black sheep of the family to be sure, disinherited, or slipped into bohemian ways, but definitely polished somewhere.

'You really are quite a surprise,' she countered LO's statement. He was quite unaware he might have caused offence. Finch gave her a big, generous grin.

'Have you ever thought about England, Peter?' LO asked.

'England?' Finch had not switched off that frank, open smile and was still unashamedly sizing up Vivien.

'To further your career.'

'No . . . Not really,' he added quickly, which caused Antonia to cough and choke on her cigarette.

110

'Surely there's nothing more to be done out here.'

'It's not so bad,' said Finch, and shot Antonia a warning stare.

'My partner, Cecil Tennant's coming out. We run my private company, LO Productions, together. Perhaps we could offer you a contract, Peter. To work for us in London.'

While Vivien had begun to shape Finch into a striking young courtier, one she could keep at her beck and call – perhaps even a little more dangerous than Dan Cunningham – this counterbid of LO's alarmed her. Why should he be allowed to have Finch all to himself? His proposal spurred her to make her own plans for him.

'Oh, so this is to be your contribution to Australian Theatre,' she spoke in her silky, mocking tone. 'To lure away their better actors. I thought you were here to inspire them.'

'Oh you've certainly managed that,' said Finch disarmingly, unaware, as Vivien saw it, of the tension between herself and LO. In any case, Finch had directed his compliment primarily at LO.

Vivien fumed. 'Isn't it nice to see the men getting on so well together!'

Finch turned, this time giving her a playful look, as if to say your turn will come. But LO ignored her.

'Vivien likes to be the centre of attention Peter – or hadn't you noticed?'

'No please . . .' Peter again attempted to turn on all his charm. She noticed how grey-green his eyes were, how good he looked close to. '. . . I'm fascinated.'

His lips moved, as if he had some idea to impart to her, but he turned again to LO, speaking rapidly, as if with a sudden flash of insight.

'Act One, Scene one. You're not supposed to be on stage.'

'Ah,' said LO, clearly delighted that his potential protégé did not appear to kowtow to fame and stardom. He possessed, too, that comic insolence, that instinctive

111

gift for timing LO felt he most needed to revive in himself. 'The man knows his Shakespeare. Not entirely successful, but you don't know till you've tried, do you . . .?'

'No I liked it . . .'

Vivien was staring at the menu. 'I think I'll order, Antonia. Then, if I'm still feeling nauseous, I can blame the food . . .'

The old proprietress shuffled up to them, deposited a bakelite tray with a pot of tea. She left steaming napkins on a plate and, when Vivien snatched at one, she scalded her hand and dropped it.

'Scarrett O'Hala,' said the old woman, who had paused behind their table and was peering at Vivien.

'Pardon?' said Vivien, recoiling with genuine mystification.

'Scarrett O'Hala?'

This admiration, this amazed recognition, instead of affecting her as homage, caught her like an unexpected reproof. She deserved it. The old woman made her feel at once contrite and humble. Towards LO she had been behaving in a completely beastly way. Whatever could Peter be thinking of her, except that she behaved like a spoilt little bitch? Like none other, that is, than Scarlett O'Hara.

With eyes lowered like a chastened school girl, an expression she knew always brought to LO a calm and gratified response, she smiled demurely at her husband.

'Australia isn't quite as remote as I thought.'

The others laughed with delight. Perhaps they were as much pleased that she had included them with her at last, as they were tickled by her wit. Even the old woman grinned toothlessly.

The same night they invited Finch to the Princes Theatre, so that he could watch the show from the vantage point of the wings. Vivien as Lady Anne in wimple and gown, showing rather more of her pectoral snowy-white skin than she would have liked, examined the actor from head to toe. He in turn – as he watched LO before his entrance as Richard III revving up his power by shaking the iron ladder – could hardly believe his eyes.

Later, having played some of her few scenes – not yet quite dead as the victim of Crookback's malevolence – she joined Finch in the wings. She waited for her next entrance.

'Oh,' she whispered with more than an appreciable edge to her voice, recklessly testing what kind of character he had. 'What a pleasant surprise!'

The irony could not have been lost on him. But it floated away without affecting him, without him giving her any sign of recognition. Were they all so innocent of nuance, so unresponsive to scorn? He just seemed to be watching and waiting.

'Hello Vivien,' he intoned, without turning his eyes from the spider-like object of his fascination, LO's body bending and twisting beneath the harsh lights.

She shifted herself a little closer to him, wondering how she could turn his head, scratch, flay, wound him in any way she could. Her disgusted tone, her intensity, betrayed the level of her engagement. Like recognises like.

'You're obsessed!'

Again he flashed her a grin which seemed the ultimate defiance of any kind of care. It made her feel greedy, hateful, desirous at all costs to make a conquest of him.

'Are you queer for him or something?'

The blood drained from his face. It had never occurred to him in a million years. He shook his head, like a powerful bull recognising at last it has been hit over the head with a sledge-hammer. 'Wot?' he half-mouthed, puzzled and frowning.

The lights crashed to black. Vivien's cat-like, blue-green eyes burned away in what little spillage there was, savouring her realisation that she had struck home.

The scene was over. She picked up her skirt, ready to sweep on to the stage. Finch cowered in the darkness of the wings and when the lights returned they revealed, for once and only temporarily, a man discomfited.

The following morning when she woke in the Windsor Hotel where she and LO had lived for more than a month now, Vivien knew her period would not come. During the previous few days – she had had the usual signs and moods – and these more than compensated for by some heavy drinking. At such times gin became her favourite. Nor had she been limiting herself to two or three.

LO sat at the dressing-table applying brilliantine to his hair, brushing it back in the same methodical and efficient way that he did everything. He gazed at himself with a dedicated, careful objectivity. It was not vanity, but the sort of scrupulousness which he, as an actor, knew better than anyone how to apply to his performance.

The bright Australian light crept around the curtains and, as sharp as cocktail sticks, picked out those sensitive gaps in her defences. The dark image of LO between herself and the dazzling brightness, mostly excluded by the drapes but hanging there as a threat, caught her attention. She liked watching him when he was not aware of her, when she could weigh up what he was, not always feel herself the object of his ever-revolving scrutiny. This power over him brought her confidence, for it was as if he trusted her, laid himself open and vulnerable to her observation, allowed her some advantage.

Someone knocked on the door. LO turned to see if it had awoken Vivien, but she had shut her eyes again. He rose from the table to open the door and, as he crossed the room, he stumbled slightly and winced in silence as his knee gave him a stab of pain.

Letting in the room-service waiter with the breakfast trolley, he observed pleasantly, 'And only twenty minutes late. A vast improvement for the wild west.'

The wild west was how he liked most of all to characterise this new country.

But the waiter, a red-headed boy with an eager, pleasant

114

face – a trainee, probably, keen to make his way – did not know how to read this mixture of jocularity and jibe. LO could not stop acting, could not tell where performance ended and real life began.

'I just bring it up, sir.'

'Of course you do. I've yet to find anybody in' – he paused, to make the most of the native delivery – 'Orstrailia personally responsible for anything.'

It was hardly the time or place to make a party political broadcast but LO, like most of the Old Vic Company, found the country quite impossibly union-ridden.

'Ah, did you want something else, sir . . .?'

'You've done all you can, I know. Thank you, young man.'

'Thank you, sir.'

The waiter left the suite by edging away backwards – still confounded by the heightened sense of reality he had encountered in the presence of LO, who now turned to the trolley and poured his tea.

'Are you awake, Bibs?'

Vivien stirred as if emerging into day for the first time.

'Come on. Char.'

'God, that sun is like daggers.'

He crossed to the bed and plumped up her pillows. She gave him a kiss on the cheek. He responded with an indulgent grin as he helped her to wriggle up higher in the bed and sit up. Her breasts, fully revealed in the loose night-dress, posed a pleasing contrast of fullness with her lightness and frailty of form. He, nearly a foot taller, and in every way stronger, darker, firmer, seemed like earth to her ethereality.

'How do you feel this morning?'

'Good.'

He handed her a cup of tea and sat down with his on the end of the bed. Vivien held her cup but did not drink.

'You don't deserve to,' he chided.

'Don't start darling . . .'

'You drank far too much Gin and It.'

115

She stretched back languidly, knowing her bodice was as open as could be. 'And had *such* a good time in the process.'

One of Vivien's strengths was that she never regretted her indulgence, never gave way to self-recrimination. On the contrary, she felt that her pleasures affirmed an aristocracy of taste.

'And you want to have a baby . . .'

She flinched. What did he know about it? Had she been blabbing the night before that her period was overdue, that they could hope again: hope the hellcat . . . Oh God, of one thing she must be sure, not to tell him before she was certain. This time she had learned her lesson. And she would stop acting. At four months if the doctor thought she should.

'You've started, haven't you?'

'Mmm . . .?'

She spotted a way to escape, otherwise she would blurt it out. She had to squash the hope.

'God!' she declared in exasperation.

He drank his tea. If Australia was the wild west, he had his own private corral, his own taming sessions with Vivien's moods. He knew the signs only too well: he had played Petruchio a hundred times opposite her Kate. He had to handle her so gently on the end of his lariat – with cups of tea, consoling words, but sometimes with a sharp jerk of command.

He drank his tea and waited. In what direction would the lightning tongue lash out?

'Talking to that idiot waiter like that . . .'

He sighed inwardly with relief. At least she was not casting doubts upon his masculinity – or his potency.

'What . . .?' he asked almost jocularly.

'You've started being hideous. I don't know how I shall stand it.'

'I really have no idea what you're talking about.'

'Richard! Richard! I saw you staring into the mirror.'

'Don't be absurd.'

116

'There it is again – that perfectly vile tone. I shan't speak to you if you go on like that.'

'You'll give yourself a headache.'

'Leave him on the stage.'

'It's not *me* who has the trouble leaving characters on stage. *You're* the one who can't take them off with your make-up.'

'But the difference is I admit it.'

'I've got nothing to admit. I'm the realist – one of us has to be.'

She had defended her position on the bed well, and, as if to concede she had driven him off, LO stood to carry his empty cup back to the trolley. He hardly noticed that he was slightly limping, for the pain from earlier had abated.

'You're the one who limps on stage – and off.'

He turned quickly. There was a faint quickening of tempo, as if the ante had been upped. 'Because I hurt my knee on stage?'

'Exactly.'

'What do you mean "Exactly"?'

'You bring your stage injuries into real life . . .'

This went on for some moments, their replies becoming sharper and more concise, till each was mirroring exactly what the other said, and both were meaningless. Vivien, vexed by the way she became more and more cornered, pushed her cup of tea, still undrunk, on to her bedside table, knocking over a phial of pills which LO snatched up as evidence.

'You're the one who needs pills to go to sleep.'

'And do you know why? Do you know why?'

Now both had the lariat around the other's neck, each sought to deflect the other's head and win dominance.

'Because I never know what you'll turn into by the morning.'

'It's not me who changes.'

'You turn into whoever you're rehearsing. You can't help yourself. That's why I need pills. It's frightening.'

117

LO stopped, adopting an eminently reasonable tone. 'Viv, you're playing Lady Anne right now – for all its worth.'

'Because you're playing Richard Crookback.'

'I'm being myself,' he insisted doggedly.

'You see – you can't tell the difference anymore.'

He almost sniffled with exasperation. 'This isn't Richard!'

As if to emphasise the point, when he now strode the thick-piled carpet there was no trace of a limp.

'It is! It is!' shouted Vivien after him. 'Look at yourself, lying and deceiving. Twisting everything I say. I hate you when . . . when you're not you.'

LO advanced on her again. If he had a lariat in one hand, and now drew himself in towards her, he had a whip in the other, a mental power which could make her cower, willing her to give in. His voice assumed the same posture of threat.

'Do you really, Puss? Do you really? Is that really true?'

He was now seriously frightening her. She quailed in front of him, blinking and swallowing. She jumped from the bed, her short night-dress well up above her knees.

'Stop it, Larry. I can't stand it. Maybe you can. I can't.'

Relentlessly he still moved in on her. But she no longer felt fear. It had slid into an area of unreality, and could be purged in what she now instinctively knew how to engineer as the sequel. It became transformed into a dance. She backed into the dressing-table. He crowded her so that she had to lean backwards. Step-dipping, she arched her back, her breasts rode up and jumped from her gown.

'You've never been satisfied with just one man Puss. Admit it. You're glad when I'm more. The more the merrier!'

He looked at himself in the mirror and fed back on himself from his reflection. She could now acknowledge that he talked both to his own reflection and to her.

'I hate it! I hate it!' she said quickly, but all the force of hate at once departed from her aroused body. 'I just want *you*,' she added quite hopelessly.

He picked her up and carried her back to the bed. Who was he now? Lord Nelson, Rhett Butler, Heathcliff? Who was she but Emma Hamilton, Scarlett O'Hara, Cathy Earnshaw? He could dominate her while not reaching out to her. She could give way by playing up to his subjugation, by surrendering herself while not trusting him with her true self.

This time she felt more secure than at other times when they indulged in these kinds of bedroom scenes from the movies. She had a secret. She thought – and was almost convinced – that she was pregnant. This time she would enhance love for both of them.

'I would I knew thy heart,' she began declaiming.

He dropped down on one knee beside her.

''Tis figured in my tongue.'

'I fear me both are false.'

'Then never man was true.'

'Well, well, put up your sword.'

Her voice was husky, thick with arousal. He kissed her passionately.

15

Elsie perked up, changing the tint of her glasses from dark brown to the lightest of blues. She sported a Jacmar headscarf inscribed in Afrikaans and English, which had been designed to commemorate the Royal Tour of South Africa in 1947.

She and the Old Vic Company were picnicking by the Yarra River outside Melbourne. The landscape around them shone like parts of Burgundy: hillside vineyards and spacious, slightly undulating, cereal fields. The difference here was that most homesteads had been built on a single storey, most were of wood, while some rested on stilts of uneven length.

LO stood on the ridge with Cecil Tennant, who had just arrived by plane from England. Tennant still wore the formal dark suit with collar and tie which he had travelled in. LO, however, had assumed a positively decadent air with an open-necked white shirt, white flannels and a straw hat. He pointed out to Cecil the English familiarity of the scene – 'A little picnic by the river' – by which he meant, of course ironically, that the scene they were witnessing, while it might have passed for a Cambridge bumps race, was a long way from sedate boating at Henley-on-Thames or Stratford-upon-Avon. The company was, in a word, drunk – half up to their waists in the river, some splashing each other with oars from boats, some just eating from tables heavy with wine and food.

LO smiled and made a slight deprecating gesture with

his hand, as if this was all he could think. 'Drinking here is compulsory, Cecil. I blame the weather.'

Although mid-winter, the day was sunny, even close. It had been raining not long before.

Those members of the company who were still in a fit state to recognise Tennant greeted him with enthusiasm. He was introduced to Antonia Vaughan, to Peter Finch – who was keeping firm control over his intake of liquor. Finch had heard of Tennant's arrival and firmly intended to impress him. Some younger members of the company, including Dan Cunningham, were so possessive of Vivien that they tried to distract her attention from Tennant.

'Cecil . . . Oh Cecil, you're here!' With cries of delight Vivien ran up from the jetty, dripping from the water fight in the boat and looking utterly wonderful.

'Vivien . . .'

She flung her arms around him and hugged him tight.

'Darling, you're going to love this place . . .'

Reluctantly extricating himself from her embrace, Tennant glanced down at the front of his suit, drenched by Vivien's dress. But she would not let him stay there, with the others, she had to have him all to herself. So, dragging him off, she made him pick up something to eat and drink, then led him down to a boat so that he could row her up river and they could be alone.

'I wish you hadn't brought that film with you, Cecil,' she remarked when Tennant had manoeuvred them round a bend and slowed down to remove his jacket.

'Why ever not?' He expressed this mildly, but his bringing from England the finished print of *Hamlet* for its first showing at the Athenaeum Cinema in Melbourne in a few days' time had been the main purpose of his trip.

'I won't be able to watch it, I know I won't.'

Vivien then launched into a diatribe against her imaginary rival, Jean Simmons: a silly school-girl, she called her, over whom LO was making a fool of himself. When Tennant tried to impress on her that the film was outstanding, she dismissed him by saying that it reminded her of such a wretched time in her life.

Adopting the role he carried off best, that of uncle and mentor to these spoilt children, Tennant recalled how vulnerable Vivien had been during the filming of *Anna Karenina*. He tried to make her think of the future rather than the past. Vivien immediately began to play up to him. He adopted more and more of the firm and reassuring masculine role – until she suddenly dropped into their talk, 'I'm hoping you're right, Cecil . . . I'm expecting.'

If he was surprised he showed no trace of it, and switched at once to congratulate Vivien heartily.

But, having blurted out her hope and fantasy – for while the period still had not come she had no positive proof – she felt a little more constrained to be truthful. 'Well, I'm expecting to be expecting.'

Next morning Tennant and LO ate their breakfast in the dining-room of the Windsor Hotel. The hotel's thick red carpet, its imperial leather armchairs, oak panelling, the black, wrought-iron elaboration of the lift shaft, made it indistinguishable from any English counterpart. LO felt eager for news of political intrigue and asked for gossip of the Old Vic Company in London.

This his friend supplied in good measure, a splendid accompaniment to the hearty breakfast both were enjoying. LO expected nothing but generous back-slapping from the Old Vic Board, for the tour was earning a huge profit. But Tennant told him that one or two members had raised objections, and ungraciously complained that LO and Ralph were behaving true to form – 'off gallivanting' – while the others did the hard grind. LO was surprised when Cecil told him that it had been Tyrone Guthrie whose voice had been the loudest in this backbiting, for Guthrie had been their firmest supporter.

Cecil then raised the matter which concerned him most deeply, Vivien.

LO resisted at first, half-joky, half-prickly. He pointed

out that it was on Ralph's suggestion that he had brought her out here in the first place. What should he do now? Take her home?

Cecil pressed his concern. Was it true that they were trying for a baby? LO laughed off this question. 'In the middle of a ten-month tour? What do you think?'

Engrossed as they were in such a delicate subject, neither saw Vivien approach the table. The early morning was often not her best time, but this morning she radiated power and beauty.

'My two favourite men.'

She kissed them, her buoyancy and happiness pulsing out waves of reassurance to both of them. LO sought out Tennant's eyes, as if to say, 'I told you so'.

But when, that same evening, they prepared for the Melbourne première of *Hamlet*, the mood had certainly worn off. The bravura of living at the limit had evaporated. The thought that she had to watch that wretched film she so hated – simply because she had not been playing Ophelia – had put Vivien in the most appalling mood.

Sylph-like, at her most vulnerable in appearance, wearing just a petticoat, she sat brushing her hair and staring at herself in her make-up mirror. She flung down the brush, rose and walked over to her chest of drawers from which she extracted a suspender belt. Slipping it on she found herself struggling a bit to fix it near the top and pulled at it savagely. The sight of LO, who in contrast was completely calm and almost ready to leave for the première – he was adjusting his shirt studs and fitting his cufflinks – provoked her into some self-pitying remark about her size.

'I like you with a bit of flesh to spare. It suits you,' LO replied crisply.

She sat down and started rolling her nylons, muttering, 'Well just as long as you're happy, I shouldn't worry, should I? I live to please my lord and master.'

LO, without allowing himself to become ruffled in the slightest, expertly tied his bow tie. He looked somewhat askance at Vivien, but then it was hardly unknown for her to throw a tantrum just before going out. She smoothed out the wrinkles in her nylons and snapped the fasteners on the suspender belt.

'The food in this country is so awfully fattening . . .'

She shuddered at how much of the butter, chops, sausages, rich puddings, and fresh milk she had devoured. She stood and craned her head round to ascertain the effect of her seams, making some final adjustment.

'How are they?'

LO glanced down.

'Spot on.'

'I don't want to end up looking like June Kelly, do I?'

'You could do a lot worse.'

He knew at once that he had answered this trick question in the wrong way, for Vivien then pointed out very suggestively. 'You like these overly healthy Australians, don't you? Male and female.'

'Come on,' he answered. 'We'll be late.' He knew the best reaction to Vivien's efforts to pick a fight was not to react at all. She stopped dressing and observed him as he brushed his evening jacket methodically. She loathed his unflappability, his sangfroid, his harmony with the impersonal world of masculine business.

'You may be.'

'I may be what?'

'Late. I'm not going.'

LO had an impulse to hit back, but resisted, biting his lip.

'Why do I have to go,' Vivien continued, 'and watch an appalling little seventeen-year-old lisp and simper her way through a part that's too good for her?'

'Because,' he replied patiently, 'half of Melbourne is waiting for you. They'll be disappointed.'

'Hard luck.'

'You're expected. Don't be silly.'

'You know something I didn't expect about you till we came to Australia is how . . . like your father you are.'

LO showed surprise. 'My father!'

'So stuffy . . . and Anglican.'

'You never met my father.'

'So observant of the forms and well-behaved – like a high church vicar.'

'Can we discuss my parent's background when we get back? The car'll be here in ten minutes.'

Here was the LO born to command, of the breed that had kept the world steady in the last half century.

'As you like, I'll wait up for you.'

But LO had reached his own limit. He did not explode in a violent Celtic passion. Anger detonated remotely in him, high in the head. He said to his wife, silkily, 'Vivien, darling, you're coming tonight, even if I have to dress you myself and push you into the car kicking and screaming.'

'Do! Do!' she shouted back. 'I've always wondered why you don't use force on me – seeing you're basically a bully.'

She was now tempting him with all her might to let go. She did not care what the consequences might be. Indeed, he did now turn to her, threateningly, with a strange vindictiveness on his face, and came towards her.

'You're afraid of expressing real passion. You save all that for the bloody stage.'

She realised that he would have loved to give her a thrashing. She too would have been more than gratified. What greater relief for her loneliness could there be than fighting? But he strode past her and pulled out from the wardrobe an evening dress which he hurled across the room at her.

'If you're not ready to walk out of that door in five minutes flat, you'll get all the passion you could wish for.'

She stared at him, only slowly understanding, feeling utter contempt. What made it worse was that, in the icy look he returned, she knew he was keeping her image intact – *his* idol, his little high church madonna, his romantic fiction.

125

16

An ordinary film première crowd, but dressed up to the nines, awaited them at the Athenaeum. But now, hovering over the well-fed faces of those that wanted to mob them, there was an element of unreality. She could see that hundreds of women wanted to touch her, or to maul him. Public celebration of love might all too easily turn into public sacrifice.

'It's them,' said the voices. 'They're coming. Here they are. Doesn't she look beautiful?'

But how LO responded. She could not but admire as he stood up, took a deep breath and smiled. She wondered if he viewed any crowd as more than a collection of extras to boost his confidence. Whether they were paid or paying, was there essentially a difference?

'Ladies and gentlemen, I will not take up much of your time. I know you are here to listen to the Prince of Denmark speak – not a mere knight of the realm.'

That he could pitch his appeal just right for whomever he addressed made Vivien shudder. She had no vulgar, popular appeal like he had except that she had the looks, the flesh, the eyes . . . only in this could she rival him.

'I just wish to mention about how a woman – a girl really – had her first taste of the wonders, the mysteries, and yes, the pain of interpreting and performing the greatest dramatist who has ever lived. The experience Jean Simmons and I shared in making the film of *Hamlet* was both rewarding and chastening. Because Shakespeare lives and

126

breathes as no other dramatist does, he has the power to get inside our soul, change the way we feel . . .'

She was an individual, what the mob ultimately hated, but she could see that LO had no individuality at all, he was nothing and everything, he slipped into every mould, he became every mirror held up to nature. The faster the times changed, the faster did LO.

'I have acted Hamlet perhaps sixty times, but because Jean Simmons had never done it before, her innocent questions made me re-examine my whole approach and technique.'

She had a chair on the stage, next to him, where he stood at the podium illuminated by an overhead light. Vivien realised that he – and she – were exclusively lit by the beam of this spotlight placed high up in the dome of the Athenaeum. Why shouldn't she let the audience concentrate all their attention on LO? she thought. It was he whom they had come to see. She crept her chair very slightly backwards and then sat well into it, so that she could retire into shadow. The sharp light now stopped at where her legs formed a right angle out from her body – her legs were all they really wanted to see, she reflected.

'That is why Shakespeare will never lose his relevance, because when we stage him, or even read him carefully, we reveal ourselves, strip away the clothes of habit and civilisation; and stand before each other naked.'

Her face, set as it had become in hurt and mortification, received new pricks of irritation from his crypto-sexual imagery. Later, when they sat in the front row of the stalls and watched LO play the 'Take thee to a nunnery' scene with Jean Simmons, she could not help fidgeting and sighing. LO turned and gave her a look of cold steel: she smiled and silently mouthed the word 'Amateur'.

'Daniel, for God's sake, get me a drink!' she whispered urgently to Cunningham at the reception in the Athenaeum foyer afterwards.

They were pressing in on her now from all sides. She

had a violent pain in her stomach. The period which she hoped would never come – had now believed would never arrive since she had missed the last a month before – was imminent.

Cunningham accepted her command with a broad grin. Vivien superventilated a loving smile, but as the flash of the cameras faded so did her smile.

'Sir Laurence, Miss Leigh. Phil Brereton of the *Melbourne Age*,' a voice said. 'I thought the film tremendous.'

'You're most kind, Mr Brereton,' said LO who, sensing that Vivien was straining to move away, caught her by the elbow.

'Miss Leigh . . .'

'You'll excuse me, won't you? It's Larry's film.' She adopted her most innocent tone of surprise. 'I wasn't in it.'

She slid away from his grip, but as she took to flight LO pursued her. Both found themselves faced by the most gorgeous society lady who had bobbed up from nowhere with her white-haired, utterly undistinguished husband in tow. He half-hid behind her, hanging back from their scrutiny.

'Sir Laurence . . . We saw you in London last year, in *Oedipus*. But honestly, this was just the best. Bruce thought so too.'

But now Bruce could not escape and he emerged from behind his wife's ample charms and forlornly shook LO's hand. Vivien caught sight of Dan holding two glasses but clearly lost for a view of her. LO again had her in a cold, steely grip, and his thin-lipped mouth was tight with determination.

'Who was that delightful girl?' asked Bruce.

'A discovery of David Lean's, Jean Simmons . . .'

'Quite exquisite.'

Cunningham had now located them. 'Excuse me, Larry . . .' he interrupted. Vivien's spirits cheered up at once. She sensed LO's hold relax. At last. She was free.

She seized the glass, submerged as much as her mouth in it as she could to take a deep gulp. 'Anyone interesting?'

'Yes,' mocked Cunningham. 'Me.'

LO shook his head with disapproval as they walked away laughing. The Mayor of Melbourne grabbed him by the arm – LO registered fury as he felt himself seized in a firm grip – and led him to where they wanted another photograph of the mayor in the actor's company.

Her satisfaction at the long sip of champagne – followed by two or three more – released in Vivien an unexpected intimacy towards Dan. She had also spotted Finch at the party, and for a moment hoped for rescue by him, but he appeared more remote, more stand-offish than ever.

'Dan, you're a treasure,' she said.

'Well, you did look rather desperate.'

'Darling, you don't know the half of it . . .'

'You have only to ask.'

This last remark pulled her up short. It was an odd remark for him to make, and warranted further inquiry, so she inquired what he might have meant.

He began to look somewhat shifty, staring down at his shoes.

'When Larry's got his hand full. When you're feeling bored . . .' Dan let the unspoken words hang in the air by way of explanation.

She *was* intrigued.

'Well, he's not the good time sort. Is he?' he continued.

'Daniel, are you perhaps suggesting something a little bit wicked?'

He pointed to her glass. 'Drink up,' he consoled her, 'and I'll get you another.'

LO's face, bobbing above or between those celebrities and functionaries who were using him to their hearts' content, kept swivelling round to where Vivien stood, his expression registering alarm and uncertainty.

Some half an hour later, the older watchdogs of the company had become just as worried as LO at the rapid intoxication which had engulfed Vivien, who was now flirting outrageously with Dan.

129

'Vivien's winding herself up again,' remarked Mercia Relph to her husband.

'You'll have to get her out of here,' said George.

'She won't listen to me.'

'I'll see if I can get a car.' He went off.

Elsie had at the same time begun circulating among the rest of the party telling the Old Vic personnel that it was time to go home. Vivien, sighting her spoil-sport or Mrs Grundy – her bête noire – said to Cunningham well within earshot of Elsie:

'If that grotesque woman tells me to go to bed I shall strangle her.'

Thick-skinned as she had grown in the execution of any matter concerning the well-being and morale of the Old Vic Company, Elsie marched up to her.

'I've spoken to Laurence,' she informed her. 'He thinks it's time we all retired.'

Vivien caught the double-meaning and sallied forth, turning to Dan to send Elsie up.

'Good gracious, Elsie, that's a bit drastic, isn't it?'

She shrieked with laughter at her own wit, although Dan, cautious and intimidated by the presence of authority, did not feel quite so brave.

'I meant, go to bed,' Elsie replied coldly.

They began to argue, till Vivien, pushed by an unrelenting general manager, grew ever more coarse, so that even Cunningham curled a lip in distaste.

George Relph returned from his quest for a car. Mercia stood behind him. But he, too, received short shrift from Vivien, and all five stood there awkwardly – she hotly defiant, Cunningham not sure which way to play it, wondering if he might not gain some dubious private ambition if he supported her. Peter Finch, sensing the deadlock, came over to them, and, asked, in his usual, understated manner, 'Is something the matter?'

'Just a bit too much excitement. You know how it is,' said George.

Vivien, suddenly putting her hand to her brow, either

130

acting or feeling complete, overwhelming nausea – she could never be sure which it was – staggered against Finch.

'Do you think perhaps . . . we could get some air?'

George's brow furrowed in consternation.

'It's all right, George, we're going to be fine,' Finch told him.

Supporting her and reassuring everyone with broad expansive smiles, Finch steered her from the room, decoying the glances directed at Vivien towards himself by his own commanding power. LO, not seeing in him a rival, but an equal – perhaps even another side of himself – showed relief as Finch took her out.

17

So why should I tie myself down to one man? she thought, feeling now a return to calm in Finch's company. Wasn't it too much of LO to ask? And hadn't the novelty worn off? She did not see why she should stop having experiences, meeting new people, exploring other sides of herself.

They had stumbled upon an old, closed-up room above the foyer, a disused greenroom it might have been, now a store for some dusty canvases, copies of old masterpieces used for stage decors. Over on the far side of the room she could make out a dirt-engrained old piano and some imitation Georgian chairs. The only light came from the street lamp outside the uncurtained window, luridly enhanced by the red and green of a winking neon sign.

'I love places like this . . . They're full of old souls. Can't you feel them?'

The repose she had begun to feel inside had not worked itself through to her outward behaviour, which was still highly dramatic. She stood theatrically in front of an old Alma Tadema-like painting of dancing slave girls. She put a finger to her lips. Her face settled into pre-Raphaelite contours.

'You can almost hear the rustle of angels' wings and the last sighs of virgins being put to the sword, dying for their chastity.'

She was making a definite pitch for his marauding instinct, but his feelings seemed contained and opposed to hers, bound up in the trust LO reposed in him: he even looked somewhat alarmed by her outlandish talk. He wondered out aloud if they should not get back to the others.

This sparked the astonishing irruption of an opposite mood in Vivien. Her face broke into different lines, and her eyes cackled as she spat out her defiance. Behind this display of fireworks, however, her mind ticked away with all the cunning she could summon. How to corrode Finch's decency, how to undermine his honesty, how to upset his loyalty – towards LO.

'Oh curse them,' she said, meaning the people she had just left in the circle bar. 'How silly and little and petty they are. They can *rot* as far as I'm concerned.'

Finch stepped back a pace or two.

'How I despise them with their twittering, idiotic conversation and their grubby intrigues and their fawning and toadying to LO and him to them. They are insects, loathsome insects.'

At this final expression of disgust she threw herself into Finch's arms, by which she was held firmly, but neutrally.

'What on earth's the matter?'

She stared up into his face. In it she saw loyalty to LO, the desire to be liked, a courteous devotion. Damn it, had she totally misjudged the man – for who *was* he like, herself or LO? She relaxed slightly in his arms, looking up at him from under her brow, trying to catch him in her net of enchantment. She purposefully delayed saying anything, trusting in their proximity to awaken in him the recklessness she had anticipated.

'Do you really want to know, Peter?'

'If you want to tell me.'

'It won't make pleasant listening.'

'Doesn't worry me.'

'I'm afraid my husband is in love with somebody else.'

She could sense that at this remark he now slightly let go inside, for he had been seeking some 'no worries' Australian formula to explain the odd situation in which she had flung herself at him. After all, husband with mistress, what could be more banal?

133

'Oh . . .' he said. 'How do you know?'

'The usual signs . . . He's not as attentive or loving to me. His mind's always on other things.'

She could tell that he was puzzled, uneasy, and that the signals he received from LO had confused him: the disciple had deep trust in his master.

'Oh yes, it is. And I could tolerate it if it was another woman . . . but it's not.' His eyes widened a shade as she let the implication of her words sink in. 'It's a man.'

She had really surprised and alarmed him now. His eyes registered a high level of incredulity.

'What . . . ?'

She paused for a moment. 'Richard.'

'? Richard . . . ?'

Australians sometimes had a way of putting question marks before words as well as after them.

'And he's not of this world.'

He flashed her a wide grin, sure she must be having some weird joke at his, or LO's, expense. Black humour was something he knew plenty about.

But she was not in the business of making pleasantries. She had never been more serious in her whole life.

'Richard who?' he asked.

'Gloucester. Richard III!'

He looked intently at her, his mind hard at work trying to read what she meant. Her gravity impressed, without doubt. Her eyes stared back at him brightly – too brightly. He realised, not without a growing sense of unease, that it was not just the drink that was talking.

LO was exercising his seigneurial right and giving Vivien a good ticking off which she parried with good-natured excuses. She felt in a much better frame of mind.

'. . . You haven't asked me what I thought of the film.'

He grunted, as the question stopped him in his tracks, and thought, 'That's rich.'

She then averred with utter and unfeigned honesty, 'I

think it the finest film I've ever seen. Your acting and direction were awesome.'

This became as complete and total an act of contrition as she could make.

'It made me feel quite small,' she continued quietly, again with a wavering voice but unwavering sincerity. She turned towards where he stood, his back to her. 'But you made a mistake in casting her, Larry, can't you see . . .'

'Her talents are quite obvious to everyone but you.'

'What *talents*? The ones that got her the part . . . ?'

He said briskly, in complete command of himself. 'I'm going to see if Cecil's up. I can't take you when you're like this.'

'The truth hurts does it . . . ?'

'For one of us it's the truth,' he said coldly. 'Don't judge others by your own standards.'

She really felt she was losing her grip on everything. The period had come. They had no baby. She was not pregnant. Could he not see? Could he not allow himself to make contact with her, with the real, lost, unhappy child who needed her own very tender and frail individuality to be respected? In Vivien's case, individuality meant a sense of pain which could so quickly become a black, damaging and inescapable cloud.

In those few words about the film she had given him her complete love, her adoration; she had trusted him with what she was. Now she could not let him go, not while there was a hope that he might see.

'Larry, please . . . I'm sorry . . .'

His tone was unemotional. 'Why do you do it, Vivien?'

'Because . . . because I don't want to lose you. Because someone's always trying to take you away.'

'If you lose me, Vivien, it won't be because of anyone else.'

She could not turn the straightness, the clear hardness of his thought into a warmth that supported her, that lifted her up. It was because, somewhere inside her, she held that he was responsible for her; she had given him everything, and it was up to him to make her feel all right. She was like a bewildered child always trusting in a parent's

135

omnipotence – at this moment, at least – completely trusting, dependent. No, he did not see this.

'Take some of your pills and go to sleep. For everybody's sake.'

He slammed the door as he left. She stared after him, at the closed door. She felt her body buckle, as uncontainable grief and despair convulsed her mind. To resist this she grabbed at her cigarettes with feverish, scrabbling fingers but her lighter refused to work. She hurled it at the mirror which cracked from side to side.

Crouching herself up, feet tucked under her thighs, she sat down to stare at her reflection. All was lost, except this image in the mirror, rivened by the crack. Once she shifted her head slightly to see if the reflection would change, but it remained distorted, not quite fitting together any more. Tears welled up in her eyes and began to course down her cheeks. She felt terribly alone.

Next day there was great consternation in the company, for Vivien sent round a note to Mercia at the theatre saying that she apologised for her behaviour the previous night, and that she was too ill to go on as Lady Anne in the evening. Vivien followed this up rapidly with her own arrival in Elsie Beyer's office, swathed in furs, wrapped in veils and shuttered by sunglasses from the cruel probing light of the sun. She carried with her an enormous bouquet of flowers, which she offered to the matronly lady before kissing her on the cheek. She made an utterly frank and sincere expression of regret for the way she had behaved, causing Elsie to feel genuinely touched, although still sorely grieved. When Vivien, having admitted that cruelty was a part of her she would never understand, left her office, Elsie had to stem her tears in an effort to appear normal and controlled.

The onus of replacing Vivien for the evening performance fell on LO. He now had to rehearse Vivien's understudy, Georgina Morgan, who threw herself into the role with great enthusiasm. A lot of whispered ill-feeling by those present at the rehearsal became directed towards Cunningham, for it was he, it was felt, who could have protected Vivien instead of encouraging her to drink.

However here, too, Vivien, anxious to redress the evil she had committed, appeared and flitted like a pale ghost among those figures dotted in seats throughout the auditorium, saying kind words to appease hurt feelings, hopeful and generous towards her understudy's talents. As she watched LO rehearsing Georgina and lightly delivering Richard's lines for Georgina to respond to, she felt an enormous burden had been lifted from her shoulders – at least for that night.

Later, just before the curtain was due to go up, Vivien called in again at the dressing-room to help Georgina on with her wimple. She noted with a smile that LO had sent his leading lady a large silver platter of oysters to boost her morale, with the message attached, 'Best thing ever for first night jitters.' Had he not done the same for her, with almost identical wording on the card? Vivien wondered what kind of first night Georgina would have? 'First night' was such an ambiguous expression. Had LO meant it ambiguously?

Passing through the foyer of the theatre to return to the Windsor, still scarved and bespectacled in anonymity, she heard the fans who waited for ticket returns discussing her absence. They did not seem to be too disappointed. 'Who cares,' said one. 'I just want to see him. He's a dream.'

Back at the hotel she settled down for a long evening on her own. Seating herself comfortably at her desk, she began a letter:

Dear New,
I hope you are feeling better than your alley-cat mother down here all by herself in Australia. Ba is not here tonight . . . so I'm feeling a bit alone . . .

She rang the bell for room service.

*   *   *

137

Five minutes later she was still writing to New when there was a knock on her door. It turned out to be an extremely handsome and athletic-looking young waiter whom she had noticed a day or two before in the foyer. He carried a silver ice bucket with a bottle of champagne. When she saw him, Vivien's mood at once switched. A sudden elation flooded her being.

'Good evening, madam,' said the boy. 'Your champagne.'

'Could you open it, please.'

Not very experienced, the boy at once set about opening the bottle. Vivien watched him, not prepared to come to his aid, but feeding off the sight of his handsome limbs and head, his immaculately groomed turn-out. Like a gold prospector who has a itch to find a nugget where everyone knows the mineral has long been exhausted, she could not resist hope. That there might be some miracle cure had become an obsession. She now almost peered into people, saying, in effect, 'Can you help me? Can you?'

The waiter smiled as he wrestled with the difficult cork.

'Is it tight?'

'Seems to be. We don't get a lot of call for champagne.'

'Do you know what days the airmail goes to Great Britain?'

'No, I'm sorry, madam. But I could find out for you.'

He smiled her a big broad grin, although his teeth were gritted as he continued to wrestle with the bottle.

Vivien gave a little laugh. 'I had no idea Australia was so far away until I came here.'

'It's a fair old distance.'

'Have you ever been to Britain?'

He shook his head, but had now disengaged the cork, which made no sound. 'I'd like to go one day.' He poured her a glass.

'It does seem quite preposterous to have a little bit of Britain stuck way down here. The people speak the same language but I expect they are very different . . . underneath.'

The boy refilled the glass which she had already emptied,

138

then returned the bottle to the ice. He tidied up the foil and napkin.

'Will that be all, madam?'

'Although I know nothing about Australian men. You're a secret lot altogether, aren't you?'

As her questions were becoming a little leading, the boy scratched his neck and began to fidget. He still waited for her to ask him to leave. Vivien lit a cigarette and swallowed several more sips from her glass.

'Would you like to share a glass of champagne with me? What's your name?'

'Er . . . Billy . . . Evans,' answered the boy hesitantly.

'Would you, Billy Evans?'

She tossed back the rest of the glass.

The boy shifted from foot to foot, his cheeks colouring a bright red.

'Er . . . We're not allowed.'

'Allowed?' she commented with a little tinny laugh. 'God, Billy, if you only did what you're allowed in this world you'd have a dull time of it. More shampoo please.'

In the theatre they were warming up for the performance. Or rather LO was, dressed and made up as Richard, nakedly flashing his sword through the air. Cunningham, in costume as Richmond, approached him warily.

'Really, it wasn't my fault . . .' he excused himself plaintively to LO.

In the wings, watching them, completely hidden in the tall shadows of the flats, stood Peter Finch. What he was doing there no one quite knew. Except that he watched.

LO flung Cunningham his sword. Cunningham caught the weapon, but the force with which it had been thrown to him – at him? – made him jump.

'See to your sword play, Daniel. Just get it right for once.'

Vivien strode about the hotel room calmly and in control. She had enslaved Billy, transferring her helplessness on to him. She was no longer the victim.

'I'm not really allowed to drink or smoke, Billy. Did you know that?'

The boy stared this way and that. A modicum of courage would have expelled him from the room in no time at all. But he remained there, tongue-tied.

Vivien put the case for the defence.

'In fact, I'm not really allowed to be me. I'm actually supposed to be somebody else.' She marched over to him and spoke to him confidentially. 'Do you know who? Do you, Billy?'

The poor boy stood there dry-mouthed, unable to utter more than 'Er . . . no.'

'I'll tell you. I'm supposed to be Lady Olivier . . . you're not allowed to . . . behave like this . . .'

She adopted the tone of her persecutors. Her chest felt constricted and she started to cough. But she went on, bravely thrusting her glass at Billy, who poured out more champagne. 'I'm meant to be a Lady. Keep myself locked up in a corset of good manners and protocol. It doesn't matter if I die. If Vivien Leigh is stifled to death. Just as long as *he* flourishes. Any allegiance to me is treason against him.'

Her eyes were now fully dilated and staring with fever. Her throat began to hurt.

On stage, in the full glare of large protruding footlights, against the vivid green of the Bosworth field backcloth, swords clashed in a desperate fight. LO, murder in his heart, fought Cunningham in a duel to the death. Finch watched from the wings, completely anonymous.

Cunningham tripped, ran away, turned this way and that, defended himself as best he could. But his face betrayed his absolute fear. The audience sat forward on the edge of their seats. It did not seem at all like acting. LO slashed and lunged, nicking Cunningham on the chin.

'Billy, we're allowed to do anything we want. Anything . . . at all . . .'

140

This did it for the boy, who figured out that if he was ever going to manage to leave that Windsor suite in one piece now had to be the time. He licked his dry lips, squared his shoulders, clucked a few noises in his throat which might have been parting pleasantries but sounded like defective speech, spun on his heel and fled. The door in front of him opened, then closed.

Vivien stared after him, her adrenalin peaking then suddenly ebbing. Her shoulders slumped, and her eyes went out. Lines of verse suddenly invaded her out of the shadows, each delivered in that clipped, incisive tone, cutting into her heart like daggers.

> Come hither, Catesby: rumour it abroad
> That Anne my wife is very grievous sick . . .

They reverberated in her brain, with LO's mocking deceitful face as Richard leering over her, staring right into that gaping void of self:

> Anne my Queen is sick, and like to die . . .

She ran to the bathroom, feeling terrible.

She retaliated by hurling her glass of champagne at the mirror. She stared at the melting mirror, liquid and strangely lined with the thrown champagne which dribbled over and down from it.

Another voice began to pound away at her, this time her own, unnaturally wrenched out of normal resonance, weirdly squeaking and booming.

> If ever he had child, abortive be it,
> Prodigious and untimely brought to light,
> Whose ugly and unnatural aspect
> May fright the hopeful mother at the view.

A grievous pain doubled her over and she clutched at her stomach. Twisting with agony she staggered away from the bathroom into her bedroom. The telephone on the other side of the bed seemed the only possible hope of salvation, but it was too far away. There she stood for some moments, swaying, unable to move, holding her belly, gasping for breath – until finally she collapsed.

18

That same night, sick with worry over Vivien, LO gave the worst performance of his career. He just could not get inside the skin of Crookback. He certainly could not love him, for his thoughts kept leaving the stage, flying back to the hotel room, apprehensive of mischief that Vivien could be wreaking on herself or others.

He did not much mind what she did to him. He could accept that. It was the pain she caused herself that he wanted to stop, for he knew that only if she had a higher regard for herself, and could go easier on herself, would she then relax sufficiently and find harmony enough to achieve the goals she had set herself.

But extremes have a knock-on effect. Extreme fatigue – such as the tour was now causing in both of them – extreme exposure, extreme party-going, extreme desire, extreme feeling. All these might feed the artist – but they destroyed the human being. And if the human being wanted to reproduce . . .

He found himself becoming so distracted during the long evening that he almost forgot his lines. His acting grew erratic. At one point Richard called for some ale. LO did not wait for it and when the lackey came on with a large glass of Australian beer – much lighter in colour than English – he found himself not knowing what he should do. He stood stock still for a few moments – there was dead silence all over the theatre – then he took the glass and drank it down. Again there was dead silence. He had not a clue what to do and let out a terrific belch that could be heard all over the theatre. Then the lines came back into his head.

Wandering around the stage, nearing his end as Richard, he could feel the energy draining away from his performance. The audience began to grow restless. As he tottered about, mumbling and raving in a subdued rage, suddenly from the back row of the gods there sounded a very authoritative voice. 'For God's sake, speak up, man!' it ordered.

It was like a voice of doom, this command, in its distinct – rather Jewish and East End of London – tone. Like someone's middle-aged, Pommie aunt. There was an immense silence all over the theatre. He stopped, looked up to where the sound came from, screwing up his eyes. He stood back. Summoned his breath and gave the next lines and the ending – 'My horse, my horse, my Kingdom for a horse' – the most blood-curdling, satanic force he could muster. By the finish everyone had forgotten the mediocre, lack-lustre performance – they only remembered the ending.

The cheering was thunderous as he bowed before the crowd and brought forward Georgina for her share of the applause. As he turned and walked upstage he saw Elsie had arrived in the wings, breathless and pale; he knew her face meant one thing and one thing only. Something had happened to Vivien.

Dammit, he cursed and swore inwardly, unable to walk off, not wanting to deny Georgina her share of the triumph, or disappoint the audience – or, worse, cause more of the speculation and backbiting in the press which had begun with the reviewer's remark that he had seen better Richard IIIs in Melbourne. The use LO then made in a speech of the Australian slang 'bonzer' and 'beaut' had provoked a ridiculous controversy over whether he was insulting his hosts.

He had to suffer his growing fear. A spectator, lodged in the fly-gallery, staring down upon the greatest actor in the world, might have remarked, seeing his plight at that moment, that his life was not so different from that of a puppet, dangled from a string and being played with by some monster.

The curtain would come down. He would rush to Elsie. Start to chat. The clamour out front would grow. The stage-hand could hold the curtain down no longer. LO would rush back, grimace, bow.

The action would repeat itself several times.

At least nothing awful had happened, so far as he could judge.

He rushed straight back to the hotel. The bedroom was dimly lit, as if poor Vivien had a terror of light and would stifle all of it if she possibly could – or at least not allow around her more than the minimum necessary. She lay in bed, heavily sedated, pallid and ill-looking, just like she had – how could he ever forget it? – during the filming of *Caesar and Cleopatra* when she had miscarried.

She recognised him as he sat on the bed and stroked her lank and sweaty hair. She looked so stricken with guilt.

'Oh I'm so sorry,' she said. 'I don't know – what – came over me.'

Her voice was so artificial and strange, again as if, like him, she was not truly master of herself.

He tried to quieten her, but wondered, with annoyance, if that was really the way. If she had some conflict, some difficulty inside her, what was the point of dampening it down, squashing it? Surely it should be allowed to breathe, grow, explode if necessary.

'I wish . . .' Vivien went on, 'I could understand . . .'

LO regarded the face of the doctor who stood near him. The doctor had given her a very heavy dose of tranquillisers, so he had been told. 'Sleep, that knits up the ravelled sleeve of care' – that was the idea, wasn't it? But this was the elusive sleep that came of its own accord. Did any chemically induced sleep knit up the ravelled sleeve of care?

'Why . . .' asked Vivien, '. . . are they punishing me?'

145

The doctor's warning glance told him that it was time to leave. She had been taken away from him, he reflected, she was beyond him, she had *placed* herself beyond any help that he could bring her. He tried to give her signs of his affection. He smiled, he pressed her hand.

LO was aware the other's eyes were fixed closely on him, watching every move, every expression. Part of him knew he could conceal what he did not want to say beneath his English gentleman exterior, his charm, his tactful evasiveness. But these Aussies weren't taken in: something to do with being colonials and then, perhaps, further back penal victims.

'Well now . . . of course not.' He smiled a dismissive smile. 'I suppose what I'm saying is I'm not surprised she "thought" she was losing a baby . . . You see, Doctor, that's what she wants. She wants it very badly – I suppose we both do.'

Again LO had this feeling of helplessness, as if his own life did not belong to himself. Perhaps this was the explanation, all along, since he had met her. Perhaps this was in the nature of a great passion, and must always be – the reality that the lovers never really belonged to one another . . . He and Vivien had once taken part in a reading at the British Embassy in Paris. He recalled some lines from a French poem they had read.

'Sire, by omnipotent God,' Iseult told her husband
'He doesn't love me, nor I him.
It was from the action of a herb I drank –
And he drank – that led us into sin . . .'

Of course sin was a ridiculous and old-fashioned concept these days . . .

'And of course we've tried. God knows . . . But regrettably she's miscarried. Twice as a matter of fact. It's all very painful.'

The doctor appeared far from sympathetic, nor did he seem much satisfied with LO's answers.

146

'Perhaps she's missed a . . .' It was clear to LO that the doctor understood what he meant.

'What can you tell me of her medical history?'

That was much easier. LO reeled off all the dates and circumstances of her attacks of tuberculosis, the treatments prescribed, the extent to which they had been successful in combating the disease. He added to these his fears that she worked far too hard and that while they had hoped the tour would be something in the nature of a holiday and rest for both of them, it had not in any way turned out like that.

'Sir Laurence, I'm bound to say,' replied the doctor when he had finished, 'that physically, despite turberculosis, I found your wife in fairly good health.'

There was something ominous in the doctor's tone. LO looked at him for a moment or two.

'The incident which has just happened. Has she had such an attack before?'

'Attack?'

'Of course it's not my field. I don't wish to play the amateur . . .'

'Are you trying to tell me she's deluded?'

The doctor smiled again at him, making him angry. That wry, distancing look of mockery. God, these people needed teaching some manners.

'I think there could be non-physical problems, yes.'

The expression raised hackles of contempt in LO. The same could be said for just about everybody in the world. Was Vivien special in that? We could all be pushed too far – everyone had a breaking point.

'As you say,' he answered curtly, 'it's not your field.'

'Sir Laurence, if such problems exist they should be attended to.'

'"A nervous disorder". Isn't that what they say? "An attack of nerves"? "Nervous exhaustion"? Well, Doctor, I can tell you that I have felt that too.' Hysteria is not the sole prerogative of woman, he wanted to add, but did not. 'We're busy people with busy lives and we're well overdue

147

for a rest. I'm grateful, of course, that you came tonight. I'm grateful for your concern. And I hope you won't think me impertinent, but I know her better than you.'

The doctor just stood there impassively, a solid, unfeeling, unriven piece of rock.

'Let me tell you,' said LO. 'She's not sick in the head or crazy, Doctor. Just somewhat indulgent . . .'

LO nodded, as if to confirm that his inner feeling accorded with this. It was, after all, what she responded to most in him – the firm hand of control. Ever since she had been a child, and because of her beauty, she had been spoilt, flattered and indulged every moment of her waking life. There was such a thing as good behaviour and bad behaviour. Her father had given her no discipline at all. Her mother had burdened her unnaturally with feelings of guilt. Her first husband had been a decent man.

But if only he himself had taken her in hand, separated in her what was self-indulgence – her madness – from her true, impeccable great quality, the power that she could have as an actress, and allowed this to live and grow. Yet sometimes, as a person, what she needed was a damn good hiding.

But what he said to the doctor was, '. . . And to tell you the truth she probably gets that from me.'

148

Part 3

19

Vivien's 'attack' occurred at the tail-end of the Melbourne season. Fortunately, at that time – in early June – they had a spell of good weather, so she and LO could pace the sandy beaches and piers of St Kilda and Brighton and inhale the sea air together.

The British Council was now making so much money from the tour that it agreed everyone should take a short holiday, after the next leg of the journey – Hobart, Tasmania – and just before they opened in Sydney. Although the rest of the company were not as tired as their leaders, and not beset in the same way by personal problems, they were still fairly exhausted and in need of a break.

On one of their walks, LO decided that Vivien, although still visibly frail, showed positive signs of return to her old self, and that he could raise the painful matter that had been on his mind.

He asked her, quite directly, why she had done what she had done, and if the reason could be because she thought she was expecting a child. That she had reacted in this way when she found out that she was not pregnant.

'Yes . . . No . . . I hoped I was,' she replied. Although perhaps a little flat and depressed, Vivien seemed to him completely normal now. 'I wanted to be pregnant. Oh how I wanted it.'

She turned to him, with that enraptured girlish appeal on her face that he always found so irresistible.

'It's what you want too, isn't it?'

He pulled himself together. He said quietly, 'Bibs,

wanting it isn't enough. Wanting it won't make it happen.'

What he meant was that they had to evolve into two different people, that they had to move on to the next stage in their lives. They had been the world's great lovers for too long: the darlings of the gods had to accept mortality – decay and change in their relationship.

But she avoided his implication. She would *not* give up. 'I must have been drinking terribly.'

The time had come to try and explain. In one sense she had to learn, also, to take responsibility for their relationship, for him – as he had for her.

'What if it's not the drinking?' he said to her. 'I doubt if you had that much. What if it's something else?'

He had meant this to convey the idea that they had to improve, but a sudden look of panic came over her face, as if he had triggered off a fear that he did not and could not see.

'I've always thought,' LO went on, 'that the well-spring in your acting was a . . . a sort of controlled hysteria. When you're in charge it's good, when you're not –'

She immediately grasped his intention.

'So if I wasn't an actress,' she said quickly, 'I'd be right as rain? It's just that I don't feel like becoming a bank clerk or an accountant to please the doctors.'

He could not challenge her with what was on the tip of his tongue to say – 'And what about a mother?' – so he consoled himself with a joke. At least they should keep in contact.

'Next time you get hysterical I'm sending you straight to accountancy school.'

She clearly felt his support in this remark for she could now apologise and reveal her own feelings about being ill. The truth was, she told him, that she could not remember what happened. She remembered lunch and then going to the theatre – but, for the rest, it was missing.

'I know there's something wrong with me, but we can fight it,' she said. 'We can fight it together. It's just a passing thing.'

At one level, LO felt relieved by her admission, her acceptance of responsibility for what had happened, for it absolved him of blame. But the talk had not gone in the way that he had hoped. He wanted so desperately to rationalise the problem in terms of his own nature. She seemed to be saying it was deeper than that.

He kissed her gently on the head, hating himself as he did so.

'You must never let them put me in hospital, Larry.'

The sense of gravity and shock inside him grew. Did she really take it all that seriously?

'And you must promise never to leave me. You must promise me that, whatever I do.'

He suddenly felt the depth of what his loneliness would be like in a life without Vivien. Not only the defeat of his hopes, all his life effort towards her – and he had to admit towards himself; to improve to realise the best in himself – but the loss of his guiding inspiration. What could he do but fill his words with all the passion and emotion at his command?

'I promise, my darling, I really promise . . .'

At first they desired a holiday on the Great Barrier Reef – an extreme notion of Vivien's which Cecil squashed by saying, 'How often have you been to Moscow for a few day's rest?' In Hobart, it had been freezing cold. They had flown there by Dakota. For their opening, in *School for Scandal*, the audience arrived at the theatre carrying blankets with them, and the cast, from behind curtains, could see their breath freezing in the air.

While some of the company stayed behind in Hobart for their holiday, LO and Vivien flew to Sydney and then north to Queensland.

They were unable to become a very private couple, even on holiday. They had asked along as guests, in the beach house they rented, several of the company including Dan Cunningham and Cecil. At Archerfield Airdrome, Brisbane, they were appalled to find that a crowd of five hundred people turned out to greet them – LO had already

153

pleaded at Mascot Airport, Sydney, for some privacy. 'We are entitled to it,' he said. 'When we are on the job we put everything into it, and we want to relax completely now.'

LO donned a white panama and dark glasses and sat on the beach reading a script which Tennant had brought with him to Australia. Vivien hid in her room at first – and wailed incessantly of her desire to return to Tasmania where she had been happy playing Lady Teazle, a role which she carried off completely without strain.

Then, one day, donning a two-piece costume which was daring for the time – with an elaborate knot just between the breasts and a small skirt to cover the tops of her thighs – she stepped out into the fierce sunlight and headed towards the sea. The sky was pure, crystal pure and blue. The sun raged through it alone, unchallenged, yet after a while LO was surprised to discover that it concealed rather than revealed. Not only did the light blind the eyes directly, but by its intensity it hid objects or made them invisible.

But unaccountably Vivien had left off her sunglasses. Now, down by the water's edge, she appeared to LO locked up in a world of her own. She could not stay still. She had to move on, spurred by discontent or that ever-changing will of hers to find something new. He reflected sadly that even a week or two before, he had seemed to know so much about her; today, fresh, recovered, sporting and playing like a young animal, completely wild and untamed, running at the tiny waves, turning and running away, she had become completely unknowable again. She had even changed to resemble like the sun itself, some inexplicable mass of fire and gas held together in cohesion, giving light and heat, but not necessarily always destined to remain in one piece.

The sun is outside us, eternally unknown, and will remain that way forever. Would it be so with Vivien, even if he were always to remain true to her in his heart?

She pranced about in the waves young and skittish like a colt. LO could enjoy, in the strange act of mental possession, the sight of her. But he could not communicate. He saw the wild joy on her face. He worried about her. He did not like what he saw. She was disturbing him more and more.

Fatigue had caught up with him. Usually he could bounce back quickly. He could resist the crowd, fling back its call for blood in its own face, assured of the self-renewing force of his own nature. Like Coriolanus, he would reveal his scars to them, only the better to place his boot upon their necks.

But this time it was different. He gave in to misery. The script he had taken down to the beach with him seemed like a crutch rather than a challenge. Soon he returned to the beach house where, with the others around him, he fell sound asleep on the couch in the living room.

Vivien, who had undergone some secret rite known only to her, who had laid upon a rock and offered up her naked self to the sun, who had bathed away all the misery and illness of the past months in just forty minutes – and who now had sea plants twisted in her hair, and bore a two-foot length of driftwood she had found floating in shallow water – came running into the beach house.

She stopped and screwed up her eyes to make out where everyone was. Tennant and Cunningham were playing chess; Peter Cushing, in the kitchen, was cooking the food for the evening.

Vivien offered her trophy to Tennant.

'Look. It's probably from the spar of a sailing ship.'

'No, Vivien, not even in Australia . . .' answered Tennant with an indulgent smile.

But Vivien had gone over to where LO slept and began to tickle his foot. When she had done this for some moments he sat up quickly.

'Do come down to the beach,' she implored. 'It's glorious.'

He spluttered and shook his head.

'How can you lie there,' she insisted, 'with all that outside?'

155

She took hold of his legs and tried to pull him off the settee. He complained, still reluctant to give up his sleep, muttering, 'I'm sure the Australians don't spend every spare moment rolling around in their great outdoors . . .'

'Come on, it's such a waste.'

'Do give it a break, Puss,' he complained, watched eagerly by Cunningham who had lost concentration on the chess and took an evil joy in the palpable moments of friction between the pair. Tennant, unimpressed by the courtship games of his old friends, captured another major piece.

A voyeuristic reporter – or even a casual onlooker – who heard of the presence of the famous pair in the locality might easily have been forgiven for believing that the sight, that evening, of a couple on horseback riding along the cliff paths could not by any stretch be other than LO and Vivien. There they rode, themselves as timeless as the featureless, unimpressive landscape, creating, at the same time partaking in, their own legend.

But Vivien was not accompanied by LO but by Cunningham, and, moreover, she was not in the least aware of her surroundings. Quite the reverse.

'I could scream!' she complained to her youthful – and still hopeful – courtier.

'Leave him to what he likes,' Dan told her, at the same time trying to orchestrate his appeal with a shifting pattern of looks and smiles, yet intending her to shoulder the responsibility for any seduction he might accomplish.

'He makes me so cross. All he really wants to do is work. What's happened to everyone's sense of fun?'

He sighed. Her animus against 'God' was about as boring as the rest of this damned country.

'Viv, we've come here to relax,' he pointed out, knowing this was far beyond his wildest hope.

'Not you as well.'

'Especially me. I'm on my best behaviour.'

'Coward.'

'I've made my peace with Larry. That's how it's going to stay. He doesn't take to you with a sword!'

'Does this mean you won't fight for me anymore?' At last she seemed to forget LO and turn her full attention on Cunningham. 'Trouble's what I know best, Dan. Surely you understand by now.'

Which was worse! LO's naked sword, or Vivien's naked blue-green eyes which now bored into his. He held them without flinching. Here was a moment he could not turn his back on. A gull screeched overhead. She inclined towards him as if she was going to kiss him.

But she swung round her horse's head and rode off in a canter. Cunningham watched her go before tugging on his rein and wearily doing his best to catch up.

The following night it was LO's turn to accompany Vivien on an outing. On foot they modestly headed along the foreshore to where on a rocky outcrop a fisherman had established a small encampment. A four-gallon kerosene tin filled with sea-water bubbled on a fire of driftwood ready to boil. Clive, the fisherman, plunged his hand into a wet sack and pulled out a crayfish. Vivien recoiled as it snapped its tail.

'Like crayfish?' asked Clive.

LO examined the fisherman's snorkel, goggles and, in particular, his flippers – he had once worn some and found their backstraps cruelly hurt his heels. Nearer the sea stood an old rod and reel which were jammed into a rock crevice; a line dipped low into the water.

'Er . . . yes. Of course,' he replied awkwardly.

'I'll put one on for yer,' said Clive, who was fair, bright-eyed and wore his hair in a crew cut. He was perky, like a local bird, impudent, moving with spasmodic self-satisfaction.

'Oh no, we couldn't possibly . . .'

Clive looked at LO as if he was crazy. 'There's plenty more where these came from. Crays and a bottla beer – drunks' special for Saturday night.'

He pointed to his half-full sack. Heading over to the

boiling water he dropped the crayfish in. Vivien gasped silently but was transfixed. The cray sank beneath the white bubbling foam, emitting its high-pitched 'song'.

LO looked at Vivien, whose identification with the poor creature in its death throes seemed complete, and he shuddered.

'That noise . . . ?'

Clive smiled. 'They sing.'

'Good God . . .' said LO, feeling squeamish.

'Better than having your guts sucked out by some bloody great octupus,' mused their sea-shore philosopher.

Vivien said in a tone of rapture, which might as easily have been mistaken for pain, 'It's singing its own last rites.'

Clive regarded her curiously from beneath his bushy blond brows. 'You're not Australian?'

'No, English actually,' said LO.

Clive gave a private grin. It made LO uneasy. But he supposed it was a change for the better from the usual cultural cringe he and Vivvy met wherever they went. This man owned the land he lived in; even if it was only a small outcrop of rock on the sea-shore. He felt no subservience.

They sat down on the rock and waited.

'It's amazing to think,' said LO, 'that here we're the same distance from the equator as the middle of the Sahara.'

Clive speared the cray with a tarnished old knife, honed down to its spine, and laid it on his chopping board, a weathered plank. He dipped the knife in sea-water, wiped it on his khaki shorts and split the crayfish down the middle.

'You're a long way from home.'

'We're here on tour.'

'Cricketers are yer?'

'No, actors.'

'Yeah, that'd be right.'

He scooped out some of the steaming white flesh. 'Here, miss. Get that into you.'

158

He gave Vivien a big piece, skewered on his knife. She raised it to her mouth.

'Careful, it's a bit on the hot side.'

'Thank you.'

She lost no time in biting into it. From the corner of her mouth a piece hung down. She licked it with her long pink tongue.

'Oh, it's delicious!'

Clive handed a piece to LO.

'Sorry, there's no beer.'

LO gestured with full mouth that Clive was already being generous enough. The fisherman gave Vivien another sizeable morsel.

'I was in England during the war,' he told them. 'Bomber command. Rear gunner.'

'Congratulations on making it through,' said LO.

'Yeah.'

He passed more of the shellfish to LO.

'I reckon Britain'd be in much better shape if you had decent tucker. Sausages, spam, mashed spud and more spam. I got really depressed in the end.'

LO, his face effectively sealed by the extreme gastronomical delight, attempted a polite grin. He admired the man's technique with his audience. Every time you wanted to say something controversial give your listeners crayfish. Soon shuts 'em up.

LO recorded every detail of the man's speech and gesture in the notebook of his memory.

'No wonder they're such a joyless pack of bastards. But who wouldn't be on snags . . .'

'Snags?' Vivien looked inquiringly at LO.

'Sausages,' he replied on the point of swallowing.

'. . . and chip butties. Nice people but – given half a chance . . .'

Inscrutably he left his last sentence half-complete, like a sawn-off shotgun, easier to conceal beneath clothing. He scraped out the last of the flesh. LO saw his action in terms of the ecclesiastical ritual of his father's old Anglo-Catholic mass – they had been very high church. He and Vivien were witnesses to the dismemberment of their traditions, and were receiving the sacrament of this new country. They turned to each other as the ocean heaved and sucked under the rocks. They did not know whether to laugh at or resent this generous fisherman given to insults and epigrams. They bit the blue air.

Next day, without fail, the sky was again blue, with a hot, hot sun. But they had progressed, LO noticed, at least as far as Vivien was concerned, from the fish stage of evolution to that of the reptile. She had become drawn to closeness and contact, and therefore, at least potentially, to repulsion. Honestly – he was driven to observe – while when they worked she fired him, stimulated him, provided a constant challenge, when they were on holiday she could not switch off or let go. Her presence became a positive irritant.

So he had withdrawn to a corner of the room, where there was a sofa and a low table. He worked at a film proposal for *Richard III*.

She played Chinese checkers at the dining-table with Cecil, Dan, and Peter Cushing. LO found his eyes drawn every now and again to the bottle of brandy on the table. Vivien seemed determined to finish it. But what could he do? Publicly rebuke her for drinking?

'Who knows,' he commented. 'Maybe sausages and spam *are* responsible for the English personality.'

'Is there a medically proven link between eating and the emotions?' asked Cecil.

'Of course there is,' said Cunningham. 'Diet has a big effect on mood. Doesn't it, Viv?'

She had an odd light in her eyes, as if hell-bent on mischief. 'I know I feel as randy as hell after chocolates.'

Her quirky, brittle tone alerted Cecil.

'What about oysters?' asked Dan.

'Yes, them as well.' She had become as naughty, as undifferentiated in moral feeling, as a child. But, unlike a child, she carried a highly volatile explosive. Her sexuality. Cecil looked faintly outraged. Cushing pulled a face: 'Chocolates and oysters . . . ? Sounds awful.'

'And smoked salmon . . . Mmm . . .'

'Why smoked salmon?' asked Cushing in a bewildered tone.

'I don't know. It just happens.'

LO watched. His silent rage accumulated. He knew what was coming. Vivien's mood swing had been pulled back to its ultimate stretch and he was right in line next time she let go. He steeled himself quietly.

'On the other hand, we've been unable to discover *any* food which does the trick for Larry.'

Cecil looked appalled, but shocking close friends was part of the frisson. Dan and Peter exchanged uneasy glances.

'It's a pity sometimes, isn't it, dear?'

'If you say so, darling.'

For him to become humiliated, he knew, would give her victory but no satisfaction, merely cruel exultation – a feeling she herself had no control over. It unloosed total anarchy in her head.

But to be restrained, however difficult it was for him, made *her* feel that part of her was still in control; part of herself could still command respect. If he gave way – if only once – it would be the end.

So he did not rise, but remained calm and unruffled. Cunningham changed the subject. Glancing down at the checkers he said, 'You had better get yours out, Viv.'

She lashed out at him, her tone savage and imperious.

'What absolute nonsense. Don't be silly. You have to let me out sometime.'

'Look,' he pleaded, 'I promise you I don't. I'll put it there and that one will stay there until I'm all across the board and there will be no ladder for you and I shall win by yards.'

'Absolute nonsense. Play your own game. Don't tell me how to play mine.'

161

Cunningham, piqued by her hurtful attack, pouted and made appeal to LO to take his side. LO switched his attention away, barely able to hide a smile: they were like children, like brother and sister who could not help but squabble. Cecil and Peter played on, but hardly in the game as the other pair fought to the death. LO felt his stomach tightening and inevitably succumbing to the tense mood of the game. When it became quite clear to Vivien that she could not win, she lost all sight of reason.

'You bloody little sneak,' she shouted at Cunningham. 'How dare you take up our invitation and then cheat at chicker-checkers.'

'What . . . ?' Cunningham almost fell backwards over his chair.

Pale, white-lipped with anger, she sat at the table, her slender arms forming a triangle, hands cupped and chalicing her face. Her eyes, half-closed, glittered a viperous green. She relished this abuse of all these men's high expectation of her. LO, the one she most wanted to push to his limit, remained steadfastly at his papers and did his best to ignore her.

'Aren't you going to stand up for me?' she addressed him.

'I don't see what I can do,' he replied mildly.

'Dan is a bloody little sneak,' she said. 'He doesn't play the game.'

Game, game? What game? LO thought. The game of life, or could she be making some indirect sexual accusation?

'Larry, do calm her down.'

The poor boy, mused LO, he was not one of life's winners: spent four years in a prisoner-of-war camp to find, on his return home, that his wife had cheated on him and gone off with another man.

Vivien, unchecked, but responsive to a change in the wind, veered crazily round, burning up her escape route.

'Don't try to come between us,' she told Dan. 'We've

been through far too much together. You'll never split us up.'

The remark defied the wildest speculation as to what she meant. Had she had an affair with Dan? Did she want one? Who knew? But this black, defiling spurt of her unconscious clouded and poisoned everyone's view. Dan goggled in amazement. Cecil cleared his throat in embarrassment. LO became like ice. Vivien, quite unashamed, swallowed another slug of brandy. She was on fire.

'Throw him out, Larry. He's a ghastly little bounder, just out to cause trouble between us.'

LO looked down at the papers strewn comfortably around him, and gathered them up, counting the number of pages.

'It's late. I think it's time we all turned in.'

'I could go to hell for all you care.'

Tiny, slender, she was now on her feet, breasts heaving under the pretty blue and green foliate pattern of her thin summer dress, rigid with self-induced righteousness.

Outside the long Queensland breakers crashed noisily on the shore. The men were speechless, the game of Chinese checkers abandoned. The lamp burning in the corner of the room had a Gauguinesque shade thrown over it – the compulsory prop in every room Vivien inhabited. She helped herself to more brandy.

'I think you've had too much already,' said LO calmly.

She moved on this as if on cue. She began to declaim. Her acting was of the kind she rarely could feel free and energetic enough to achieve on stage. Fuelled by the confidence of her madness, the power of her emotion ran through her like sixty-thousand volts.

'As if you had any concept of what too much is. You don't even know what enough is. I've never had enough. Never in my whole life. Let alone too much. Why are men so afraid?'

She mimicked her husband. '"It's late. I think it's time we turned in." It's time we all started telling the truth.' Her tiny, powerful frame shook as she scoffed at the assembled men. 'Or have you had enough of that too?'

She stood over them like an avenging angel, while they sat sprawled, mouths open, stunned and shattered. Only LO, an old hand at dealing with Vivien's anarchy – he still veered between sympathy and clinical observation – had remained intact. He could, after all, make use of all this – sometime, somewhere. He was the witness. She had ended her speech by trying to draw him out. But he kept silent. Behind him the waves exploded on the sea-shore, one after another.

'Heavens . . .' remarked Tennant, glancing down at his watch and speaking as if his line had been written by an inept scriptwriter to break the spell '. . . is that the time?'

Dan laughed in recognition. 'Early start tomorrow, remember,' he chimed in. The 'hols' were over, it was back to school.

'I'm going to get some fresh air. It's stifling in here,' said the tragic queen.

Before the boys could react further, she had slipped her sandals off. At the door she turned, with a proud, contemptuous toss of the head, gave their stupefied shapes a last look. She dropped her sandals to the floor, where they were followed by the foolish stares of her admirers. LO rose from his chair, put aside his papers in an orderly fashion.

'Excuse me, gentlemen.'

He could see her shaking out her curly dark hair in the stiff on-shore breeze from the sea. He had to fight that desire of his emotions to abandon her. The great rhythm and ringing of the breakers could easily have obliterated all feeling from him and turned his soul into a moonlit hollow.

This was what happened. In the absence of some definite and specific male force she wanted to give herself to the ocean. Taking deep breaths she walked towards the phosphorescent deep. The wind carried away some of the emotional burden. She hardly paused in lifting up her flimsy dress over her head to greet on her naked skin the thin spume of breaking waves that flew to meet her. She ignored the beach sign which warned against the dangerous current.

LO halted in front of the notice board. The thud, the pulse of the waves cautioned him. Did he really want to take his acts of salvation as far as this? So many times he had abandoned what he was doing in the middle of the night – left meetings, run a whole range of heroic deeds to save his loved one from the dragons, the devils and demons of herself. And had he not himself had his own fair share of lives, narrow escapes, remarkable injuries sustained, deadly skirmishes outflanked? Had not the time come at last to throw in the towel, let nature or fate follow its own course, withdraw once and for all his godlike protection?

Vivien unhooked her bra and let it fall. She passed little barriers of strange transparences and jelly-like lucencies, the white cottony foam that marked the edge of the water. Soon she was into two or three inches of the receding wash. With a thumb she expertly peeled off her panties, stepped from them and left them to float away. She could not stop now. She advanced to meet her lord and master.

LO hurled a blood-chilling appeal to her.

'Stop it, Vivien! Now!'

She turned. 'Why so concerned all of a sudden, Larry? Your problems will soon be over.'

She was ten yards ahead of him. He started wading into the water after her, stripping himself, too, of his clothes.

'For Christ's sake, Vivien, it's dangerous.'

Now, crutch-deep in water, Vivien's thigh and stomach muscles tightened and she gasped as the chill water found her genitals. A moment or two later she launched herself easily into the hammer-strokes of the exploding waves, shivering with shock as she came out the other side, where at last she began to tolerate the cold. She swam out to the open sea with a leisurely breast stroke.

LO dived in and followed her, soon catching up. He grabbed her shoulder and as they bobbed up and down some twenty yards out where the groundswell started peaking to form the breakers, she turned to face him. They rode up and down easily.

'Stop, Viv. There's a current off here.'

'Who cares?'

'Come back.'

'To what?'

LO tried to answer but filled his mouth with water instead. Lordship, mastership, was now what it was all about. This was hardly the time for discussion.

'To that?'

Summary action was needed. They were two fierce and opposing currents. Now they were swept away in a third, bigger than both of them. He put his arm around her neck and struck out side-stroke for the shore. Vivien struggled to keep her mouth out of the water, but soon swallowed some and spluttered.

'You're drowning me.'

'It's the only right I have left.'

This foray of humour hit the right place. Vivien started to laugh and cough and splutter. She gave up her mutiny. Of course she did not really believe in his lordship over her. But she liked being manhandled. She renounced her homesickness for death.

But LO could feel an icy clutch from below, fear clawing at his bowels, a helplessness in his feet and legs. He struck out harder and more powerfully than before but soon came to a complete standstill, only just holding his own against being further swept out to sea.

'How glorious,' exulted Vivien, relishing the fight between her two champions.

'It's serious,' he gasped.

'I know.'

They were talking of different things.

'God, it's strong.'

He thought of the bright transparent bladders on the sea-shore. Their delicacy, their tranquility. And this creature hungering after oblivion, this Eurydice half in love with easeful death – whom nothing less than rape by the God of the Underworld would satisfy. He fought for the margin of safety.

'Made it,' he said when at last he knew he trod safer water.

He was striding from the sea he had tamed. He carried his naked Vivien in his arms, her white opalescent limbs glowing with love and promise, with rapture and sweetness in her face as she stared up at him. She reached up and kissed him hard on the lips. He stumbled, suddenly blurred in mind and displaced in balance. She slid out of his arms and lay waiting for him in that wettish unreal world of frailest sea-glass, that utter haven of deliverance.

Can one blame a man for giving way to such a tempting vision? She whimpered and cooed huskily as he tried to deliver a reprimand. Ready to settle for an alternative 'death' she was determined not to lose a moment. As she chewed her lip and her eyes narrowed as she gathered for her sweet spasm, he might have reflected, 'And who is master now?'

20

To be wanted by her in this way: she was like an eighteen-year-old girl who, unsure of herself, created a temporary self-esteem by pulling into bed with her the men whom others admired. How ever could you build a permanent relationship on that?

He began to ask himself a load of questions that you don't ask when you are in a sublime condition of ecstasy.

'I'll take her back home with me,' Cecil offered again.

LO declined, saying that she would not go, and regretted the break by the sea. What he began to turn over more and more frequently in his mind was the burdensome realisation that without him she could not survive. If ever he left her, he might have to arrange a successor.

They had at least sixty performances to play in Sydney. There was nothing to do for the present. They rented a flat in fashionable Cremorne, unpacked their luggage and tried to settle in for the night. But the apartment had no heating, no hot water, and nothing with which to cook meals late at night after the show. The only thing about it Vivien liked was that on the drive to and from the theatre they crossed the great suspension bridge and had a magnificent view of the water.

Next day they were in the Hotel Australia. Even here, because of fuel restrictions, they found the central heating limited to two hours' use a day, and they were not allowed to switch it on themselves. But they could get meals and hot water at all times.

Once more, this time with greater wariness, they had to put themselves on show. The great lovers had arrived in town. They were featured in all the newsreels. Vivien, who 'looked like a piece of gossamer' or 'made you think of a lovely pear', told one reporter she was thinking of taking a jerboa back to England as a present for Ralph Richardson. She would have preferred a platypus but they cost about forty pounds a week in worms. She was already buying gum trees and ferns for Notley.

LO continued smiling through a barrage of forthright and prying questions: the journalists did everything but play football with them.

The first night of *School for Scandal* became the great occasion of the Sydney season – the deepest bow and scrape of Australian deference, the ultimate act of homage to British culture. Five of the notables in the audience wore silk hats; one woman had three white humming birds pinned across the back of her head; another wore as a cap two vivid pink and blue birds.

After the final curtain and six calls, when the whole audience rose to their feet and cheered enthusiastically, LO addressed them:

'We have been a long time coming here, but tonight has been a joy to us all. We thank you deeply for your wonderful reception. We feel this play could be better perpetrated, but it could never be more nobly received.'

But then – completely unexpected, completely unprepared for – the greatest blow of the season fell.

Outside the Tivoli Theatre one morning Cecil saw LO's hired Humber pulling up beside the foyer. LO tumbled out muttering to himself and headed towards the door. He looked absolutely furious. Cecil caught up with him and found a sheet of paper being thrust at him.

'Read this,' said LO.

It was a cable which Cecil accepted with trepidation.

'It's from the board of the Old Vic. From Lord Esher,' said LO between clenched teeth. An idle, curious crowd had collected in front of the door. LO remained completely indifferent to the presence of so many strangers.

'I've been fired, Cecil. I've been given the bloody boot.'

It was Tennant's turn to be stunned. 'But they can't . . .' he expostulated.

LO gave way to a complete rage such as few had witnessed in him.

'Here I am,' he shouted, 'at the back of beyond, trying to forge a National Theatre, and this is how they thank me . . .'

'But it's monstrous . . .' sympathised Tennant.

'It's not just me, Cecil. They've sacked the three of us. Ralphie and Burrell as well.'

He shook with uncontrollable fury. But suddenly his knee gave way. It collapsed under him. The old injury. He gave a gasp of agony.

Cecil grabbed an arm to support him. 'Are you all right?'

'It's this blasted Richard Crookback,' LO spat, baring his teeth. 'I'm an invalid again.'

That same night the theatre was dark – they opened again the next night in *The Skin of Our Teeth*. Vivien took the Humber by herself over to the west side of Circular Quai. The driver soon turned off into some dark streets of Old Sydney and stopped in front of dilapidated buildings which looked to Vivien as if they dated back to the eighteenth century. Between these ran a narrow gravelled drive where she walked on her tall, doll-like heels and felt their straps tugging away at her ankles. She arrived at a Victorian folly partly hidden by tall, nodding palms and other extravagant vegetation which had leaves like monstrous fans and bark speckled like the snake in the Sherlock Holmes story.

Called Marsden Lodge, the building had been the eccentric folly of the black sheep of a famous mining family. When Vivien and her chauffeur had circumvented the potholes and rang the door bell, she saw it was not so large as she first imagined. The house had castellated features, massive stone buttresses and fearsomely baroque decorations in wrought iron; paintings of knights, dragons, damsels in distress, hung tucked away in discreet niches in the porch. A huge marble fountain with a crocodile spouting water gave the dilapidated entrance a somewhat slimy, reptilian atmosphere.

Finch appeared from behind the fountain. The place was so ill-lit Vivien started: he looked for a moment so insolent, so louche and devilish.

'Where's Larry?' he asked.

Vivien told the chauffeur to leave. 'There's been some dreadful business I'm afraid, Peter. He just couldn't find the time. He does apologise.'

She noticed how hurt Peter suddenly looked: a stab of competitive feeling made her head shake slightly, imperceptible perhaps to all but the most careful observer.

'Oh no . . .' Peter scratched his head. 'Well, never mind. I hope it's nothing too serious.'

'It's the end of the world, as far as Larry's concerned. So you'll just have to make do with me this evening. He was so looking forward to meeting your wife.'

She spoke with indifference towards LO's devastating news. She now turned her attention to her surroundings – a frankly pornographic painting of Venus and Adonis which hung in front of her.

'What on earth is this? Your home? I don't mean to be rude.'

'Not at all,' said Finch. 'Some mad millionaire built it for his bride but she ran off with someone else.'

'Who lives here now?'

'Artists . . . ratbags . . .' he grinned, '. . . mates of mine.'

They passed through a submerged and ill-lit, but evangelically potent vestry – or so Vivien felt it was, its effect that of a sudden gust of uplifting cold air on a sultry oppressive day – to a private chapel. Over in a corner stood a black mahogany piano. At this sat a pasty-faced overweight musician called Vernon, laboriously copying out orchestrations in a manuscript book.

171

The chapel was full of bric-à-brac and memorabilia in every shape and form: a stuffed three-foot bear, 'nigger' money boxes, old ventriloquist dummies, a propellor from a Spitfire, crossed sculling oars.

At their arrival Vernon jumped up.

'This doesn't look like Tamara,' said Vivien.

'Don't look too closely,' replied Finch.

Vivien, at her most queenly, smiled graciously, as the pot-belly of the man shook and his bald and greasy crown deferred to her presence. He seemed too frightened even to meet her eyes.

'How do you do er . . . Mrs er . . . Let me get you a drink. Champagne?' gabbled Vernon when they had been introduced.

'Lovely. Thank you.'

Some of Vernon's confusion affected Vivien. If Finch had been counting on LO, she had been counting on Tamara. She noticed, at the far end of the chapel, and beneath a grimy, stained-glass window, a table laid for three.

'Is Tamara still coming?' she asked, adjusting her snood.

'I'm afraid not. She's working tonight . . . A last-minute thing.'

The musician made a clumsy waiter and, after the premature ejaculation of a cork from its bottle, showered them with champagne.

'And so Vernon is dining with us instead?' she made a comic show of dusting away the foam.

Finch appeared tongue-tied. Vernon stepped in to cover his chief's embarrassment.

'Ah no, Viv . . . um . . . I'm just helping Finchy out with the dinner . . . like.'

She held the sticky glass of champagne, threading Vernon's beady, over-tired eyes on a string. 'Oh . . . You're going to serve?'

'Uhhh, yeah. That right, Finchy?'

Finch had returned to being a dark and inscrutable shadow. From its cover he gave an almost imperceptible

172

nod. Vivien, now at her most grand and patronising, smiled with amusement.

'What a bizarre and intriguing entertainment you've organised Mr Finch. It's certainly the most original of the tour.'

Finch slipped away to the back of his cave, an octopus about to enter the dark recess of a pool and never be seen again.

'Well, it's rather more of an improvisation than I planned.'

Vivien laughed warmly. The die was cast, and had fallen smiles upwards. The hazards were still to come.

'I thought I'd fallen down a rabbit hole for a minute.'

Finch laughed. Vernon frowned with confusion, vainly struggling to see the joke. To him this was all perfectly normal.

The candles flickered unevenly. They were alone at the table. Vivien kept wondering about this man whom fate had thrown into a strange position of intimacy with her. Like the country, he was so familiar and yet nothing she said to him seemed able to make him reveal to her what he really was. Of one thing she was sure, however: he did care. The posture of indifference was only skin-deep. Beneath it he possessed a kind of Restoration awareness of rank and money. For all his proclaimed insolence he had none of the American, gum-chewing, slob warmth – none of the schmaltz. There was a rigid sense of hierarchy – beneath all the contempt for hierarchy.

They ate simple roast chicken, drank Australian Beaujolais and duelled like accomplished wits.

'Do you know you're the first Australian man I've had dinner with alone?'

Of course she was acting in Sheridan, he in Molière, so that they might have been merely playing their parts.

'I'll do all I can to make the occasion a memorable one.'

'What did you have in mind?'

'I never have anything in mind . . . for a lady I don't know.'

'And you're convinced I'm a lady?'

'As convinced as Debrett's Peerage.'

'A husband's knighthood guarantees nothing about the wife.'

'It's my experience that not even marriage guarantees anything about the wife.'

'Are you referring to your own?'

'Amongst other things.'

They retired to their corners and smiled at one another. He toasted her with her glass. She upped with her rapier and came forward to probe his defences a little more subtly and slowly.

'I wonder what Tamara would have to say about that . . . if she were here.'

Earlier she had felt disconcerted by not knowing Tamara, and by not being able to size up the competition – if competition it was. Now she felt that she had complete control of this handsome man's appendage, could expand and contract her image to suit.

She certainly touched on Finch's chauvinist core. No subtleties here, she decided.

'But would it be the truth?'

'I always tell the truth when I'm quoting other people.'

'And when you're expressing yourself?'

So where actually were his boundaries? she wondered. Was he just an out-and-out philanderer, or were there some more rich shades of self-hood and soul to be discovered. Was he to become 'an experience', or merely something she could spread on her toast at breakfast? The dilemma delighted her, especially as she could play with it openly and make it sparkle intellectually.

Here was a reality she supremely enjoyed, a high plateau of humour and possibility removed from pain. Oh, if only one could take oneself off and live forever in Restoration times.

His ripostes had just the right weight.

'And when expressing yourself?' she repeated.

'A situation which always leads, I've found, to trouble.'

'Why?'

'I . . . er . . . I don't know.'

'I'm sure you do.'

He nodded, as if to acknowledge that he would not pull wool over this woman's eyes. The assailant was up to his weight.

'Largely because I find it hard to do what I say I'll do.'

'Very candid of you to admit dishonesty so early on in our acquaintance.'

'It's not dishonesty, I never tell lies.'

'You just can't keep your word.'

'I *can* keep it. It's just that events seem to overtake me and . . .'

He looked around to where, in the shadows, Vernon hovered. Vivien's eyes followed him.

'Ah, so you don't even break your word, events break it for you.'

He attacked with an eager disarming smile, both palms open.

'Yes.'

'Mr Finch, I fear you are a scoundrel.'

His large, dark eyes ran all over her head and shoulders, like lightly touching fingers. He asked, slyly, 'Does this mean your husband won't offer me a job?'

'On the contrary, it ensures he will.'

He posed a question with those same eyes. 'Why?'

'It is only by surrounding himself with scoundrels that his grasp of the truth seems at all respectable.'

He then asked, with down-to-earth directness, 'We have covered a lot of ground, Vivien. You've discovered dishonesty in me and confessed it in your husband. Where do you stand in all this?'

She could even win this one. 'I *lie*, Mr Finch,' she answered. 'I always have. It's what I do best.'

There was by now no doubt that physical suggestiveness had entered their joust. She meant this pun to be deliberately saucy – as well as to refer to her gift for psychological perception.

Finch frowned. He seemed to stumble.

'Do you mean you tell lies or . . .'

'That is something you will have to find out for yourself.'

Vernon, unable to contain himself further in the distant crevices of the room, emerged, bottle at the ready in an unconsciously phallic gesture.

'More wine, Finchy?'

LO had closeted himself with June in the theatre office and was trying to get through to Ralph Richardson in Hollywood. He had spent nearly three-quarters of an hour on the telephone. At last he heard the familiar, yet faint, voice at the other end.

'Ralphie . . . Ralphie . . . is that you?' He put up a hand to stop June typing.

Ralph cracked his usual jokes and pleasantries and placed himself entirely on LO's side with regard to the vehement response that June typed up for the Old Vic governors. More fatalistic by nature, he was not nearly as cut up about the whole thing as LO. He played it down in his usual way, as if he understood the indignant response of Esher and the others to having two directors, both actor knights, out of the country at the same time. But then he was not working for the Old Vic, instead earning fistfuls of dollars.

He asked after Vivien. After all, it had been his idea that they should go to Australia to improve her health. The silence before LO's reply became even lengthier than justified by the time required for the words to pass under the Pacific Ocean. LO's voice came through high, brisk, and clattering.

'Well enough Ralphie, well enough. She's out on the town with some local actor tonight. She gets terribly bored with all this.'

After he put down the phone LO hardly paused to consider the implications of what he had said about Vivien.

He turned to his ferocious dictation to June Kelly. The counter-offensive against the Old Vic board was under way.

Finch and Vivien danced to music from a gramophone. Vernon cleared away dishes, glancing uneasily at the pair. They had left the chapel and gone outside, by the empty swimming pool, where, relaxed and gracefully moving in harmony, they became as appreciative of their physical empathy as earlier they had been of their spirited meeting of minds.

Finch attempted to kiss her, but playfully she resisted: her eyes, on the other hand, said something entirely different.

21

The staff of the Tivoli Theatre, joined – or stiffened – by Peter Finch, played the Old Vic Company at cricket. Finch was batting with another member of the Tivoli staff. Vivien, who had no interest whatsoever in cricket, came as a spectator, and sat on a rug together with Georgina and Mercia. Finch's rugged ability dominated the game. Cunningham bowled but could not dampen down the Australian actor's zestful sixes and fours. Vivien applauded vigorously, until Mercia and Georgina noticed her flattering participation in the spirit of the game.

'Peter's very dashing,' remarked Georgina.

'Yes, isn't he,' answered Vivien.

'Where's Larry?' Mercia asked, in a cagey, meaningful way.

'Up to his eyes as usual,' sighed Vivien.

Finch slammed another ball to the boundary, exciting a general surge of applause.

After a while he was out, caught by Cushing.

'A cavalier forty-two, Peter,' Vivien warmly applauded his performance as he joined her. 'A pity your wife wasn't here to see you.'

'We do seem to be having bad luck with both our spouses, don't we?' Finch replied and both of them smirked at the falseness of the observation.

Vivien rebuked him for not telling her before that he was so good.

'I've always been pretty fierce at the crease,' he

remarked with a smile which told her that he was no longer thinking about cricket.

In the foyer of the Hotel Australia, LO said goodbye to Cecil. He apologised for Vivien's absence.

'She's still at the cricket with Peter Finch.'

'Oh, I see . . .'

'He's been marvellous all through this. He's taken her everywhere. It's done her the world of good.'

LO had just been injected with morphine to ease the pain in his knee. His face was haggard, his eyes tense, and he rested on a crutch. He worried far more about Tennant's forthcoming meetings with members of the Old Vic board than about Vivien's behaviour with Peter Finch. He had a performance of *Richard III* to get through that night. He toyed with the idea of playing it on a crutch.

'Just remember, if Burrell weakens you're to cable me straight away.'

'Of course.'

The two old friends shook hands.

'Well goodbye, Larry,' said Tennant. 'And good luck. Obviously you're not the jealous kind.'

LO reacted by furrowing his brow, but then laughed at what he assumed to be a joke.

'What . . . of Peter Finch?' He seemed to find Tennant's suggestion amusing. 'I'm just grateful he had the time.'

Tennant did not appear reassured by his reaction and left his unspoken response hanging in the air. LO called after him exhortative goodbyes. But then stopped to ponder seriously for the first time, the question of his wife and Peter Finch.

Darkness descended on the city of Sydney. The sky went yellow and pale azure, while the low table-land into which the harbour intruded squatted dark-looking and sad, as if lost on the face of the earth. The cricketers had all but deserted the springy thick-matted turf of the ground. Finch and Vivien lingered behind.

They chatted for a moment about winning and losing, but that former confidence which had elated and sustained Vivien left her. She felt panic. She felt vacancy. But a devil-may-care exultancy seized Finch. Anything could happen.

It grows dark early during the Sydney winter. Vivien had entered the second winter of her year. She was dying for a drink.

She asked Finch to accompany her to the theatre where she indicated she kept some gin.

'Are you superstitious?' she inquired on their arrival.

'No.'

'I am.'

Their white faces and hands flashed eerily as they walked down the aisle of the darkened auditorium. The Tivoli had a haunted atmosphere, an underdark of voodoo and mystery which seemed to operate on Vivien all the more potently now that it stood empty. A gust of evening breeze made the curtain shake, while the gangways and timber joists in the fly-gallery creaked and rattled.

When they reached the front of the stalls Vivien stopped and pointed upwards.

'I sometimes think that all the parts we play . . . that have ever been played in a theatre . . . roost up there like bats.'

They climbed the steps at the side of the stage and made their way to the centre where they gazed upon the serried ranks of empty seats. Here were more ghosts: the hydra-headed monster nightly decapitated but nightly refurnished with new faces. Vivien shuddered and thought of something else.

'When you're coming to grips with a new part,' she asked Peter, 'do you change much?'

'People tell me I stay the same old rat-bag. Do you?'

She had grown tentative, so unsure of what she thought that night. 'Larry says I do . . .' she answered with a questioning, almost sceptical look.

'And you don't believe him?'

'I don't think he's a good judge. He changes so much himself . . . though he won't admit it.'

He smiled. She again found herself hating that hero-worship of his, that deferential awareness of rank between himself and LO.

'Well, are you coming or aren't you?' she asked him abruptly, as she heard staff arriving to open the theatre for the evening performance. She was delighted to note that the smile lost its smugness and solidity, and tipped his face into uncertainty and apprehension.

LO's hump, doublet and black hose hung on the back of the dressing-room door like a sleeping Cerberus. Finch eyed it warily. More reassuring to him was the framed and mounted photograph on the table of LO making his great leap upon Claudius in the film of *Hamlet*.

He chatted on about this, a subject which bored Vivien, who wondered why he now held back, when all she wanted was some deeper intimacy, something from him that would break down that barrier of loneliness inside her, free her from her mounting sense of pain and anxiety.

She made a sally or two about LO. Finch defended him.

'But then you don't think I'm nasty?' she asked him, worried that she had put herself in an unpleasant light.

'Not at all.'

'I am to him,' she confessed.

'Why?'

She shrugged her shoulders, and stuck her hands deeper in the pockets of her white coat, which, in the harsh, dressing-room light, and with her pale make-up, gave to her face a mask-like beauty.

'It's a mystery. He brings out the worst in me and I bring out the worst in him.'

'It doesn't show.'

'We can have the most wonderful times together.'

'Just as long as they outnumber the bad.'

'They usually happen together. It's always worst when we do this play . . .' And she suddenly turned on the hump dangling on the back of the door, so that Peter winced, as the sight of it rekindled the terror it had first awoken in him.

'Blush, blush,' she declaimed, 'thou lump of foul deformity.'

The shift in her tone frightened him, overcoming his own scruples. If the costume had been for him a friendly chaperone – even a genial but warning policeman – for her it represented something more sinister, like a gaoler, even a sadistic torturer.

He crossed and placed a comforting hand on her shoulder, which she turned and kissed. Thank God, she said to herself, for she so wanted him on her side.

'I'm glad you're here, Peter. I get so impossibly lonely at times.'

He smiled and she noticed that some of the caution, the wariness had returned to his eyes.

'We'd better have that drink.'

She rose from where she was seated to fetch the gin from a cupboard and proceeded to slosh it into a couple of glasses. She grew aware that he watched every move she made, as if, she imagined, calculating the effect of any wrong step.

But did she care? She wanted to restore that defiance she once sensed in him. LO had stimulated in him a different and wider kind of ambition. So they were at war here, too, in the heart of this handsome young stranger, whom both, in their own way, wanted to possess. Well, she would have him first . . .

'Here.' She referred him to his glass, which he took and rose to toast her and which she acknowledged. All the time his eyes remained on hers as if his mind was set. She returned his look without any equivocation. She felt a thrill. Over the edge of death.

He leant down to kiss her lightly, although she would have sworn that his eyes glancingly caught the image of LO as Hamlet in the photograph.

'There. I've done it.'

'Yes, you have.'

He took her hand and led her over to the sofa where they might sit down together. If LO was her religion, she intended to sin defiantly, in full view of its paraphernalia. A last look at Richard III's suspended hump would have found it vibrant almost glowing with outrage.

LO crackled with fury. But to her it seemed all so tedious and remote, like something that happened last year. She remembered Ralph Richardson's polite and considerate remonstrations as Karenin. They made her feel kindness towards his hurt feelings, even if Karenin never came near to understanding her needs.

LO was forthright, vulgar, and bloody angry. Anyway, she loved him so why did he make her feel so guilty over staying out late for a drink with Peter? He had forced this loneliness on her.

'I thought you wanted me out of the way,' she told him. 'God knows, you've been happy enough till now.'

'Women always confuse men's active engagement in something with their happiness,' he said forcefully. 'I've been busy. So that's no excuse.'

'What am I supposed to do? Sit round here and watch while you fight your stupid battles?'

'You don't know what you're talking about,' he said in a dismissive tone.

That's it, she thought, I don't share his ambition, and this is the truth. But she wished she had his sense of purpose and ability to sink himself in what he was doing. She had a strange, poisonous, masculine rivalry trapped in that enticing and distracting exterior of hers. No identification with his aims, but a desperate wish to possess his equipment to achieve her own.

At the same time she felt the whole romantic and yearning need to be valued for herself, protected, seen and valued for what she was; not just snapped up, appreciated through the flaws in another person's make-up – as *his* trophy, *his* support, *his* wife.

'Would you fight like that for me?' she asked him.

'. . . I'm going to bed,' he said.

'Would you?'

He turned on her, still limping she noticed, his eyes blazing. 'Is that what you're trying to provoke? Have I got myself a rival?'

'I'm not made of stone,' she appealed to him. 'I need attention too.'

She then felt that something had destroyed his resistance: in just a few weeks it had gone. His way of standing up to her had crumbled.

'Well,' he said, 'thankfully you've found an Aussie mate.' His tone was pleasant, if only mockingly so. 'I'm sure he'll give you all you want.'

With these words he left her. She stood there feeling too battered even to cry.

22

Something had gone definitely wrong. Whatever she was – imperious and predatory queen or eternal protégée – had never fully become established. She was now being forced to become the supplicant to each of those she had made rival courtiers for her love.

This was only too evident when she called on Finch at a rehearsal of a new play in a tiny ramshackle playhouse miles out in the Sydney suburbs. He did not expect her, and when, bursting with fretfulness and fury, she walked in on him, she found him in the stalls necking quite un-ashamedly with a pretty young actress.

He had a hand on her breast inside her jumper. When he saw Vivien he hardly made much effort to take it out. His eyes betrayed a wicked intent to compromise them both: the actress looked startled and bashful, she herself felt humiliated and *old*.

'Sorry, Peter. I didn't realise you were rehearsing,' she remarked cuttingly – with some of the tone LO had been using on her.

'Hello, Vivien,' said Finch, flashing her one of his most disarming and laid-back smiles.

She stared at him, seeking reassurance from her own sense of betrayal.

'Er . . . This is Valda Smale.' He introduced the girl.

He did not proceed further, for the young actress jumped to her feet and smoothed down her rucked-up bra. Finch also stood.

'Hello,' said Valda.

'Pleased to meet you,' said Vivien.

'I'd best be going,' said Valda.

'Bye, Valda,' added Finch with unnecessary haste.

She looked at him with reproach. Vivien and he made it quite clear they had no further use for her. She smiled tightly at Vivien and clattered off. Finch crossed over to where Vivien stood.

'I'm very pleased to see you again, Vivien.'

She would not be swayed by this penitent move. As for the diffidence, she knew it was feigned. This treacherous, smiling Aussie bastard – oh, she could see what he was up to now. She would make rings round him.

'Are you?'

She wanted her silence to sting him and it did. He retreated into compliments.

'I enjoyed our evening together more than I can say.'

She said nothing.

'I wanted to get in touch with you . . . without being indiscreet . . .'

'I thought you thrived on indiscretion,' she said pointedly.

'Only when there's nothing at stake.'

'Oh?' Did he seek to excuse himself with the little trollop he was fondling?

'I would do nothing to threaten our . . .'

'Our . . . ?' she picked up the word with more than a hint of sarcasm.

'Well . . . us . . .' he plodded on, labouring, for her, how much she meant etc . . .

'Why?'

'Because I like you.'

She resisted his simple, unaffected tone.

'Among others?'

'No, before others,' he said quickly. 'How do *you* feel?'

'Why do you think I'm here?'

He shrugged with that typical Aussie quality of putting himself out of count. The old blankness, the old indifference.

186

'Maybe just boredom . . . getting to know the natives.'

'No.'

There it showed again; just as soon as he seemed really not to care – but while remaining genial – she became moved by him again. She wanted him again, and she could see that he wanted her.

'Just be my friend for a minute, Peter. Would that be too much to ask?'

She looked imploringly into his eyes, as if to say, 'Please, please, protect me – most of all from myself. You know I'll give myself to you, if you ask me. But please don't ask me.'

She could see that her request bewildered him: she had dashed his downbeat masculinity into the ground. Well, the Australian character had a high tolerance of flatness, of sameness. It knew where to find victory in defeat.

'Of course . . .' he said almost in nasal parody of emotional desolation. 'I'll be anything you want me to be.'

Finch fidgeted as he waited for LO in the hotel bar on the first floor. There were other symptoms, too, of a guilty conscience: he glanced frequently at his watch. He swallowed several nervous sips from his drink and put it down.

When LO arrived, limping more than had been his recent need, haggard and more than usually spitting out his words like machine-gun fire – as if he wanted the interview to be over before it had begun. Finch searched his face for clues as to his frame of mind. LO gave none away.

'Peter,' he barked, 'so good of you to come at such short notice!'

'That's all right, Laurence,' Finch replied, playing his response with as much easy familiarity as he could.

'We should have discussed it before, but the opportunity didn't present itself.' LO eased himself down into an armchair. Finch tried to smile, but the effect was cheesy.

'Yes.'

187

'You seemed to be spending all your time with my wife.'

Here was direct and frontal attack. Finch tried to defeat it.

'Er . . . did I?'

The two men's eyes met. Finch's wanted to stray, but LO held them in his own. He continued, in a crisp and business-like tone. 'The ABC have asked Viv and me to do a reading and we want you to join us.'

Finch blinked in relief. A moment of testing and danger to himself and Vivien had passed. He gave LO a great big boyish grin, unaware of the consequences if LO could read him like an open book.

'We intend to include some Australian poetry with the Shakespeare and we'd like you to choose it.'

'I'll be in that . . . with pleasure,' warbled Finch.

A steward arrived for their order.

'Whisky, Laurence?' Finch offered.

'Why not?'

'A double and another beer for me, John.'

The waiter retired. Finch spread himself in his chair looking pleased.

'Yes, I need some proof spirit to wash out a few wounds . . .'

The words caught Finch and he stiffened a second time. He seemed to become aware that he was not out of the wood at all; that he was, moreover, continually giving himself away.

LO fixed him with a penetrating stare.

'Painful wound . . . Betrayal hurts, doesn't it?'

'Oh?' said Finch, hiding away his shaking hands in his coat pockets.

'I've just had a rather nasty piece of news. Knocked the stuffing out of me.'

He left his companion dangling on the end of his silence for a few moments. Finch's lower lip began to quiver; he could feel beads of sweat forming in his hair.

'After all these years,' mused LO, 'to be treated like this. Bloody bureaucrats.'

Finch could now hardly speak. He asked, in a high and squeaky voice, 'What bureaucrats are those?'

'The Old Vic board of governors has sacked me.'

Relief appeared on Finch's face. The fluctuations were plain for anyone to see, but not picked up by LO.

'What did you do?' asked Finch.

'Nothing . . .'

'Aren't you . . . too important to sack?'

LO smiled ruefully. 'Finch . . . Finch. How naïve of you. All artists are hostages to fortune.'

The waiter appeared with their glasses.

'Let's drink deep, my dear fellow, and wish a plague on their houses.' He seized hold of his glass and with alacrity Finch threw a note on the tray, smiling at the man to keep the change. LO acknowledged the gift of the drink and raised his glass.

'To LO Productions, which has become all the more important now that I'm freelance once more.'

'I'm sorry really . . .'

'Don't be,' LO interrupted him. Purpose had concealed his observation and now at last LO came to the crunch. If he was to be sacked he would have to form his own company. He was tired of being a leading man and wanted to direct and run the show. He needed a replacement, a fine young heroic actor . . . himself but ten years younger. 'Let's talk about the future. You're still available to join us in England?'

'You bet,' said Finch. 'Tamara and I will scrape the fare together somehow.'

If he was angling for mercenary support, LO did not notice.

'You're exactly what the stuffy West End needs at the moment . . . a bit of fresh blood.'

LO smiled companionably at Finch and Finch smiled back. They even looked smug together, as if sure of their future success, while Finch beamed satisfaction at basking again in the great man's approval.

'Are you and Vivien still hitting it off?' asked LO.

The question descended like a hammer-blow on his rebuilt confidence. Could he not construe the whole meeting as being engineered to lead up to this? There was no sign of malice or jealous intent in LO's expression. He asked the question in a mild and enquiring tone and, indeed, the look LO gave him over the top of his glass seemed both friendly and concerned. But then, the man was a great actor . . .

'Yes . . . I think so . . .' replied Finch in a non-committal but worried tone.

'Ah . . .' said LO.

'At least on my part . . .'

'Good,' commented the older man opaquely. He sucked another sip from his drink. Finch was frying again.

'Why? Has Vivien said something?'

'Heavens no,' answered LO gently.

To parry LO's friendly glance at him Finch had to manufacture a smile.

'She doesn't have to. I can tell.'

Finch looked at him sharply. Who could be told? Finch's alertness signalled that he expected LO to continue. He conveyed the idea that he was willing him to: he was determined to find out what he knew.

'What can you tell?' asked Finch.

'Vivien is quite a lonely person, strange to say. She finds it hard to make friends. I mean real friends. I know she is looking for friendship from you.'

'I'd like to be friends with you both,' Finch ventured cautiously.

'She's not like other women, Peter. She can be damned hard to follow sometimes. Do one thing and mean another. You have to understand that.'

'I know she's very special.'

'Yes, I just thought I better warn you.'

LO finished his little homily with just the same amount of friendly warmth with which he began it. There were ominous undertones, no doubt, but what exactly did they imply? Finch's physical posture revealed that he did not

190

know what to think of this. His shoulders hunched slightly forward. The man was too deep for him or so absurdly superficial that his lightness of touch could not be taken at face value.

Finch stared at him fixedly. If there was hostility in this stance LO, once again, chose not to respond to it. The two men continued to stare at one another, Finch set more than ever on not being the first to drop his eyes. LO suddenly burst into laughter, showing the venereal gap between his two front teeth.

'Come on, dear boy, you look as grim as a fish. Let's have another drink and talk about the broadcast!'

The celebration of love between Romeo, played by Peter Finch, and Juliet played by Vivien Leigh, was not an idea the latter much relished. From her face one might deduce that she was being forced to drink a different kind of poison from that prescribed in the play.

She turned to LO in the middle of the broadcast rehearsal and complained how ghastly it was; she had never felt less like a fourteen-year-old virgin in her life. When reassured by him that she was doing it beautifully, she appealed to her partner to tell her how awful she was.

But he, too, in conspiracy with his mentor, passed judgement that she was excellent. Upon this she exploded in fury and used appalling language which had the radio ops and producer on their feet staring wide-eyed in disbelief through their glass partition.

LO moved almost automatically into his pilot-of-hysteria role. Discernible in his voice was a faint air of condescension, as he outlined to her in a superior way that a more mature reading did not in any way destroy the lines. Shakespeare merited an infinite variety of interpretations.

Finch concurred. 'It's the best reading I've heard in a long time. It has real depth . . . complexity.'

Rigid with anger at the way they ganged up on her, she told Peter, 'You don't have to agree with him just because he might offer you a job.'

When she played the speech again she spoke it directly to the microphone, not to Romeo. Her parting shot to Finch before the countdown to recording: 'The most attractive thing about Australians is they have minds of their own. Don't throw away one of your few advantages.'

She had occasion to attack Finch even more vehemently, later in the day as she drove with LO to a British League rally. LO was telling her why he wanted the young actor in his new London company.

'He's ideal for us. Just what we need. A lead with real strength.'

'That's a matter of opinion . . .'

'You've changed your tune – I thought you liked him.'

'My initial enthusiasm wasn't confirmed. He's limited.'

'Of course he's limited. I don't see him doing the classics. But he's got ten times the presence of most young leads in London.'

'Then book him, Larry,' she said in a peeved tone. 'It's your company. You'll do what you want.'

LO gave her a long and hard look. The strength of her reaction shocked him.

'I assure you I'm not going to force him.'

'How can you tell the Australians to build a National Theatre, then steal their finest actor?'

'Oh, so now he's their finest actor.'

'Leave him here, Larry. Leave things alone. You don't know where to stop.'

He studied her as she glared out of the window of the Humber. He then said to her, quietly, 'What's brought this on?'

'Please. I don't want another argument.'

'What are you up to?' he asked in that tone she hated.

She turned to face him. 'I could ask you the same question.'

He stroked his chin, as if finding her question completely incomprehensible.

'You accuse me of spending too much time with Peter,

then you woo him like a long-lost friend. One moment you approve – it keeps me busy – and then I'm being selfish.'

'I was upset when Cecil left. You should have said goodbye.'

She became more emphatic. 'Should I, Larry? Is that what you think? And what about me. Was I upset?'

If he had no reply it was because he was beginning to make some appalling realisation about himself and Vivien. It had been staring him in the face for a long time. Why had he not begun before now to see what had been happening?

'I can't act the way you want me to. I don't know what you want.'

'I don't want anything,' he said in a dark voice.

'I'll make my own decisions Larry, and I'll hold my own opinions.'

'Good . . .'

A moment of silence followed. Both had their own thoughts, but after a moment or two Vivien began to voice hers as if he was not even there – and in the nature of a vow.

'And I'll do what I think I must . . .'

This woke LO from his own painful reveries. But before he could challenge her they were pulling into their destination, a civic centre where a crowd of several hundred had collected. These admirers, as soon as they spotted their car, sent up a huge cheer and pressed in on all sides. Although the eager handshaking and obtaining of autographs was both friendly and decorous, even the most restrained attention had now become for both of them an enormous ordeal. They were being stripped of their flesh.

She had to make the break with Peter clean and firm and at once. Too soon she would come upon the gap of continuity, the threat of isolation. All conquest, from that point of view, was empty and arrived at nothing. He would take it well, she was sure of that, and with a kind of ironical stoicism.

193

She invited him for a walk in order to tell him. He suggested the gap on Sydney Harbour, a little too dramatic for her liking, a little too dangerous and rugged. The fall to the rocks below to where the waves crashed with random power excited thoughts different from the cool and measured ones she intended. Nor was she in any way prepared for his tenacious grip on her feelings. He seemed hurt and at a loss, naked and unashamed in the way he wanted to cling on to her. He pleaded with her.

'Peter, I can't,' she told him as kindly as she could. 'It's impossible.'

'But we get on so well together.'

'Too well. That's the problem.'

'You said we could just be friends.'

'I don't trust you, Peter. I don't trust myself. If I don't do something now it will be too late.'

'Larry's said something, hasn't he?'

'No.'

He stared out to sea in an aggrieved way. She thrust her arm through his. She did not want to hurt him.

'Peter, listen. I love him. And I'll do nothing to jeopardise our marriage. We've been through too much together. He's the constant in my life. He keeps me sane. If I lost him I'd lose my mind.'

She would now witness the limits of Finch's love for her: for if he truly cared for her herself – rather than his own subjective feelings towards her – would he not see she was speaking the truth?

'Don't look so disappointed.'

He behaved like an irritated child. He picked up a piece of loose rock, threw it down and watched it shatter fifty feet below on the shore. Did he think she was playing with his feelings? He confirmed this when he said, 'I usually break the hearts!' and then 'I was hoping you thought more of me than this.'

She tried to stop him being so cross with himself. 'Peter . . . Don't . . . You'll forget me in a week.'

This made him turn to her with shining frankness and

simplicity in his expression. 'I'm afraid not, Vivien. It hurts more than I thought possible.'

She wished he had not spoken these words. For no one knew more about pain than she did. Others might have more talent, more honesty, more truth, but let no one challenge her in her own field – that of suffering.

'It hurts *me*,' she replied, almost as a threat.

He refused to believe her. 'Does it?' he asked in an incredulous tone.

'Yes, it does,' she repeated, as indeed it did. Suddenly she felt the most enormous sense of panic descend on her. He was crushing her, and he had to believe her or she could not breathe.

'No doubt a little West End glamour will take the pain away.'

It was the same with both of them, wasn't it? Why could they only see her through the flaws in their own egos?

She believed in more, she had to have more. She believed there were cases of people who loved one another so intensely that they could burn through those layers of opacity and see each other's naked hearts. She had seen LO's. She had seen Peter's.

'You must think me a very slight person. I love you and I love Larry, and I suffer . . . terribly.'

But his distortion of her grew and grew, it became a monstrous size. He was angry at the suggestion that somehow her emotions were of a higher calibre than his. She was stealing his scene. However, all he could stutter out was, 'Really?'

'You know what irritates me about you Australians is you're so smug. You think you're the only real people around . . . Just because we dress for dinner and have better diction, you think we're empty-headed fools.'

'I just don't like you waltzing into my life, turning me inside out and waltzing out again . . . weeping crocodile tears.'

This was the final straw, the ultimate affront. This accusation that she was false made her cave right in. Her face puckered; she could feel the wild overwhelming sense of despair that clutched at her and that on all accounts she had to flee from. Flight was the only answer. It would have been better if he had called her a whore, raped her, than charged her with lack of feeling.

She bent under the rail that protected the unwary from the cliff edge and hurtled towards the edge leaping crevices as nimbly as a goat, pulling at her skirt to avoid tripping. Finch's eyes widened in disbelief as he realised what she might do.

'Jesus, Vivien. Stop!' he called out. 'Stop it.' He was terrified and at his wits' end.

She did stop, to address withering contempt at him. 'Why? I'll bounce, won't I?'

He tried his old stockman's touch with wild animals. 'Take it easy,' he crooned.

Suddenly she turned completely manic.

'Get away from me,' she screamed. 'You bastard . . . Get away from me.'

She had dropped her coat on the path to the cliff edge. Now, in a crazed run she moved further from him, she started tearing off her red shirt, ripping away the straps of her petticoat.

'No one can take Larry away from me. No one!!' she shouted.

Finch went right after her. He slipped, almost toppled down a crevice and fought hard to scramble up the other side. The rocks began to split and crumble beneath his feet.

Vivien watched him struggle without the slightest feeling of pity. She even came forward, with curiosity, to regard his plight. She exulted. Her spell over him was complete.

Part 4

23

She wanted LO back desperately. Survival – both as an actress and as a person – depended on it. But what if he had, as she feared more and more, really moved on, translating the playing of *Richard III* into the action of his own life? Did he no longer truly love acting, and was he not, by establishing himself in the realm of power, giving up the vital connection that had been made between them, the connection that mattered most.

For the deepest reality of their lives was that they were two actors: they basked, they bathed, they lived in the fluid of constant change.

Other people did not have feelings in the same way that they had feelings . . .

She was dressed as the bathing-belle Sabina in *Skin of Our Teeth*. They were in Brisbane, and spring was in the air. The daffodils were in bloom on the banks of the Brisbane River.

She loved this part – that of the *femme fatale* recurrent in the history of mankind. She had to progress through a variety of roles. Her first costume was that of a maid in a cheeky black dress with a frilly white apron. She could giggle and flirt and stick out her behind like a little duckling.

Then she played the beauty queen, in satin pants, daring tight bodice, fish-net stockings, pulling out every brazen and coquettish stop she knew to make her body as enticing as possible.

'. . . Miss Vitamin B,' the papers called her as she

'flaunted her allure among the male members of the Society of Mammals'.

LO played the lover Antrobus, and she felt that she and LO had never acted so closely together, leaving little to the imagination in Wilder's pastiche of everything from *Hellzapoppin* to *Finnegan's Wake*.

She came so near to him, she could hear his heart beating. She could show that life was made just for the two of them, and they existed on a different plane from ordinary mortals. Other people didn't have feelings. And the only two real virtues in life were power and pleasure. Otherwise it stank. This was Sabina's message to Antrobus.

She could sense instinctively that not only did the hundreds in the front of the house love it, so did LO. All the brittleness, the fragility, the insecurity, inside her had gone. She was fully alive. She was LO's equal, and each fed one another in vital, throbbing union.

'So – come here!' she moved closer. They kissed in public celebration of their love. She could feel all the company watching from the wings, the whole audience sitting out front, participating in their communion. It did not matter that she was flaunting herself, selling cheap what was most dear, because she was also buying cheap the most precious thing in life – LO's love.

She kissed him feelingly and he responded. She laid low the ghost of Richard, defeated the devil inside him. The kiss went on and on. Tonight they would give them their money's worth.

Back in Sydney, Tamara Finch knocked on the door of the chapel in Marsden Lodge: someone inside was thumping hell out of an untuned piano. At first her knocking went ignored. Then the weird cacophony of sounds suddenly ceased. The brutalising forearms went limp. The face of Vernon appeared round the door, as he opened it up.

'Hello, Vernon. Have you got Finch in there?'

'Got him. My dear Tamara, I would sooner have dengue fever. I will show you where he mopes.'

He led the actor's wife across the overgrown courtyard to where Finch and Vivien had danced some nights before. In daylight the disused and weed-infested swimming pool carried few romantic trappings. Half-full of stagnant water the pool could boast of only one occupant: an empty gin bottle which floated lopsidedly on its surface. A stone splashed into the water an inch or two away, but failed to smash it.

Finch sat on the edge of the pool, dangling his legs over the side. His face was covered in stubble, his clothes were rumpled and grubby. Next to him rested another, nearly empty bottle of gin. On his other side he had made a neat pile of stones. He shied another one of these at the bottle and hit it with a dull clink but failed to break it.

Vernon ushered Tamara over to where the great man sat, intoning in his best manner, 'Finch, visitors.'

For a moment Finch hoped it might be Vivien. He turned eagerly round, his face instantly and completely transformed from dereliction into joy. But, seeing who it was, he lapsed at once into gloom, his features grew downcast and he turned back to his desultory and wanton game.

Tamara walked over slowly to him. 'I wish you would come home now and then.'

He ignored her words, picked up the gin and took a swig from the bottle.

'I'm not going to wait forever,' she said. 'I've got better things to do with my life.'

He turned a morose, withdrawn expression half towards her. He pouted childishly.

'You're going to have to make a choice, Peter . . . You can run around like some unkempt tomcat – after anything on heat if that's your idea of freedom – or you can come home . . .'

She scrutinised his face. She waited for some reaction. None came for the time being. She would try again.

'Frankly, I don't mind either way. I married you because you were exciting . . . fun to be with . . . at the moment you're just a love-sick drongo . . . pathetic and boring.'

Finch still said nothing. His mouth fell open. He had no response to make. Tamara sighed and pulled her shoulders up as if to take herself off.

'Don't leave it too long. Tamara won't be there to kiss it better.'

She turned away to go, but some irresistible force made her swing round to look at him once more.

'How did you get so filthy?'

She did not seek the way by which she had come, but found a garden gate by which to escape. Finch picked up another stone from his pile, aimed it, and flung it with all his strength. It smashed into the floating bottle and sank it. His face creased with a huge inane grin of satisfaction.

The revelry did not cease after that triumphant performance of *Skin of Our Teeth* but went on into the night, for the company gave a surprise party for LO and Vivien. He wore white tie and tails; she looked beautiful in a long pale-green silk gown and a mink stole.

The company poured out their gratitude. Apart from their personal trials and tribulations, LO and Vivien had behaved as a perfect father and mother to their supporting players. They had nurtured them without sparing themselves, neglected neither their birthdays, nor their ailments, nor their good or bad reviews.

As the eighth anniversary of their marriage fell that day the company cheered them eight times, and gave them a present of six crystal glasses and two decanters. Vivien, not to be outdone, produced a handbag and started distributing her own little gifts to individual members.

Early next morning, Vivien, freshly dressed and full of energy, tried to spur everyone into leaving as soon as possible for a picnic in the rainforest. She trod daintily among the abandoned debris of the celebrations seeking her friends, but each of them, when located, refused to stir.

Dan Cunningham in particular, relegated to the extreme margin of her attentions, would not even emerge from under the silly hat in which he had passed out asleep some hours before.

Although it was only eight o'clock the sun beat cruelly down.

Only LO could finally be goaded into accompanying her. Rubbing the sleep from his eyes and stifling a yawn he sat at the wheel of their Mercedes convertible. He pulled down the broad-brimmed panama low over his forehead to stop the sun biting into it. Vivien, seated next to him, had not slept a wink and had spent the last two hours diving in and out of her colossal Elizabeth Arden make-up case. If there was any trace of wear or fatigue, it was well hidden. Her eyes shone with joy and she was as bright and excited as a schoolgirl on her first outing with a beau.

The engine roared with life. Vivien turned to smile radiantly at LO who did his level best to disguise his almost terminal exhaustion.

Soon they had left what remained of any track or road and drove up a rough track through a forest of majestic hardwoods. The dazzling light was now excluded. Vivien hung over the door of the car to catch the breeze in her face.

They pulled into a clearing to eat their picnic. But once they were stationary Vivien leapt from the car and vanished into the moist and steamy undergrowth. LO struggled along behind carrying the enormous wicker hamper. Soon Vivien entered a world of her own.

'Vivien . . . Vivien, where are you?' LO called after her. He struggled down a slope wondering how on earth they would eat all the food he carried. He placed the hamper on the ground and sank down beside it.

She heard him but pressed ahead without answering, pushing aside the fleshy leaves of the acacias and strangler figs, soaking her blouse and skin with dew, happy at long last to be in these Elysian fields where she could press herself against tree trunk and fern, leave the broken world of man and passion, and enter a purer mysticism of the senses.

'Vivien!' sounded his increasingly feeble voice in pursuit of her.

Again she did not respond. Reaching a bubbling waterfall with a translucent pool at its lower end she stopped, bending down to splash her bare arms and shoulders with the deliciously cool water from the stream. Suddenly she gave a start. On the other rocky bank, a goanna, its head reared up above the high boulder on which it sat, fixed her with its rigid stare.

She fluttered for a moment. She hung in the air like a loose live nerve, undecided whether to scream or run for it, or obey her impulse and give in, become a sympathetic, harmonious part of the whole.

The second set of impulses won and she settled into some aboriginal acceptance of danger, squatting there, staring back with a passive smile at the goanna; calm now that she was at one with herself and the primordial world.

The more mundane and self-protective LO, failing to find her, had lain down and fallen straight to sleep. Suddenly, without warning, the forest became like the end of the world. Lightning flashed. Thunder reverberated in deep echoing crashes through the hardwoods. The heavens opened and rain poured in waves through the leafy canopy, splashing noisily on the ground.

Instantly drenched to the skin, LO sat up with a start. Even alone he reacted as if he had an audience among the trees: a comedian by instinct he spoke aloud, with just the right edge in his voice, 'Oh . . . marvellous . . .' He stood up and called out much more urgently than before, 'Vivien!'

24

The rain bucketed down; the trees roared and snarled in the wind; the pair struggled together on the muddy slope, fighting their way back to the car. The wicker hamper had been abandoned, for LO had enough work on his hands trying to haul Vivien behind him. Her face smudged with mud, her eyes danced with delight. She was in her element.

If she was all sympathetic drive, he was all check. He tried to put a coat round her shoulders, while she declared how glorious it was. He dragged her backwards while she wanted to go forwards and eat the picnic or at least drink the wine. He told her she was feverish while she had never felt so well and in tune with herself. He felt to her like the heavy opposite pole of all she was.

At last they reached their car and collapsed into the front seats. LO, still indifferent to the poetry of their circumstances, set out trying to start the engine, but it did not respond.

'Damn,' he said.

'I'm glad the others didn't come,' said Vivien.

'No doubt, so are they,' said LO.

She ignored his irony. Quivering with excitement, while struggling out of the wet blouse beneath the coat LO had put round her shoulders she let her eyes make her meaning plain to him.

'Isn't it why we came here. To be together?'

He looked over at her, drips of water still forming under his chin. 'Vivien, I'm exhausted. We had less than four hours' sleep.'

'Who needs sleep?' she answered.

'I do. Every night . . . Frequently and regularly . . .'

'Don't be so conventional.'

He dragged a rug around his shoulders to stop himself shivering.

'We're stranded. We're marooned!' exulted Vivien.

'Stop it, Viv, you're raving,' said LO.

She was not in the least offended. 'Like a lunatic, raving mad,' she echoed him with warm colours but little edge in her voice. He did not answer. It was a little too close to the bone.

'Do I excite you Larry?'

'You exhaust me, Vivien, you always have.'

'Isn't that exciting?'

'No!'

'It must be something?' Vivien fixed her eyes on him before she went on. 'I've watched you, Larry. I've watched you feed. I've watched you take your fill. You devour me and I make you new.'

There was no resentment in her tone. LO sighed and swept back his hair which, although dampish, had been spared most of the deluge by the panama.

'Then why do I feel so old?' he answered her. 'I like the way I am. On the whole I'm content with myself. If only you were too.'

'But I am.'

He did not respond. He just looked at the rain which streamed down the car windows in sheets.

'God, I hate this country.'

'Forget about the rain. It's dry in here.'

Her naked arms reached out to him from under the big coat as she kissed him gently. He smiled, a sad wistful smile and looked into her eyes. She had raised her little tent then and there. Inside the car. The tent quietened all doubt and brought peace to her. Here was the food she needed for the moment to make her new and she devoured it.

*   *   *

In Brisbane the company had been challenged to another cricket match. LO discussed with Elsie whether they were up to playing this when they already had eight performances a week, when Vivien breezed into his office and demanded that she should be taken out shopping.

LO told her he could not because he had too much paperwork to do, and he was, anyway, still fighting his dismissal from the Old Vic Company. She poured scorn on his loyalty, but then he told her that there was more bad news. This time from Notley. Faltering and with weakening heart she pressed him to know it. He answered that her cat, New, had been run over.

This stopped her dead in her tracks. If she had been told her child had died it might not have meant so much to her.

'Mercifully swift, I'm told,' LO went on. 'He didn't suffer.'

Completely smitten she became speechless with the shock. Oh God, she thought, how he could deliver a hammer-blow without feeling. Finding contact difficult he always ran from it if he could.

'Poor old thing . . .' He joked. 'That's the way it goes with cats . . . I've told them to get you another.'

Straight away her shock turned to guilt and remorse. She should never have gone away and left New at Notley on her own. To him it might just be a cat, but to her it was like the loss of part of her soul. She turned on her heel and vanished from his office. She wanted to be on her own to mourn.

'It's only a cat, Vivien . . .' he called after her. And then, half to himself and as a joke – putting, as it were, their respective misery in context – he added wryly, 'The car however, was driven by Tyrone Guthrie.'

That evening Vivien demanded to know her future. She was in the costume of Sabina, playing the character's – and her own – most heightened state of provocative sexuality.

Mercia Relph, dressed as a gipsy fortune teller in a voluminous skirt answered with a click of the throat.

207

Sabina countered that *she* would tell the fortune teller her future.

Vivien laughed creamily and traced it out with one finger on the palm of her hand. She described how she would win the beauty contest in Atlantic City and she would go on to win the beauty contest of the whole world.

LO, as Antrobus, now President of the United States, waited in the wings ready to enter. He watched Vivien without expression.

In the front stalls of the theatre a venerable couple behaved in quite the reverse fashion, pressing themselves back into their seats as if to distance themselves from the steamy performance given by Vivien. The matron stole a look at her husband who, seeing his wife's disapproval, concurred with slightly less wholeheartedness.

Sabina was saying how she would take President Antrobus away from his wife, and that she would throw the whole married order of the world into total confusion.

The fortune teller clicked her throat.

Sabina continued expounding a philosophy with which Vivien entirely agreed. She would make every husband so gasp with desire they would fall against lamp-posts . . .

The matron in the front row gasped and addressed her spouse in a loud whisper.

'How can Sir Laurence allow it?'

The old man, whose lips watered and whose ears rang from the unaccustomed racing of his blood, croaked, 'It's a disgrace' – but he meant the opposite.

Olivier watched dotingly in the background. When the scene ended the old man clapped loudly but was elbowed into silence by his wife.

She had never felt quite so full of joy as when she tripped, almost dancing, along the backstage corridors to her dressing-room. Everything inside her felt secure and settled – and for the good. Nothing would ever destroy her again: she was like Sabina, with all those quick, wonderful changes of mood that so liberated her. And now, after the show, she would have LO to herself: true, he was never in much of a good mood after this play. He did not like his own performance, which he felt was uneven and unfinished.

But she convinced herself he would be in a good mood tonight. The wearisome tour was at last approaching its end. In a month or so, after a flying trip to New Zealand, they would sail back, this time over the Pacific and through the Panama canal. They woud have time to be together again, time to start another child . . .

Her dressing-room was dimly lit: but she saw flowers everywhere, Queensland spring flowers, hibiscus, magnolia, giant lilies. The whole of the room's light was concentrated on this rich profusion that filled the centre.

Instinctively, whatever her mood, she responded to beauty, whether of human or natural kind. Even at her most suicidal a small and perfect arrangement of stone, the lock of a child's hair, the particular soft scent of an English rose, never failed to take her out of herself. When she returned after the experience of delight to her negative feelings it was always with some infusion of hope, some strength or love to combat the nihilism.

But this excessive display fell on her when she was already carried away in transports of joy. It became like a crowning of all the loveliness she had ever experienced. She clattered forward eagerly on Sabina's high heels to inhale the perfume.

She heard the sound of a footstep behind her. She turned to see a figure, dark against the sole and single lamp that had been left on for the blooms.

'Oh Ba, darling,' she gasped ecstatically. 'They're gorgeous.'

But as she gathered to propel herself into his arms she felt an icy shadow steal over that delight and joy, and with a final and chilling sound shut it up forever. She could not believe what her ears told her.

'Hello, Vivien,' said the voice.

It was Finch. She had to blink several times to wake

herself up. But she remained cloaked in the nightmare, for such she was sure it was.

'I hope you like them.'

So they were his. Her vitriol and scorn scorched those blooms and all at once the room seemed to fill with the smell of smoke, of limp, withered, festering lilies.

'Peter, you must go.' Her voice came back to her at last, a fluttering of hope and resuscitated love.

'I've only just arrived,' he answered in his most facetious and buoyant manner.

'Peter, please leave.'

'I don't understand.'

'Why don't you understand? I don't want you.'

'But I didn't come for you . . .'

What could he mean? Perplexed, shattered by this sudden drop from her height of bliss into some slimy pit of reptilian threat, thrown back upon herself into despair, she bit her lip, frowned while she fought to contain her feelings.

'Didn't Larry tell you?'

'Tell me . . .?' she echoed in a hollow tone. She swallowed the lump in her throat – but it stuck there. She closed her eyes but the fixing of the lids shut out nothing. Why had she gone on remorselessly and ceaselessly shutting down the realisation which was forming inside her all along? Why blinded herself to the all-too-evident truth?

'I've come to sign my contract with LO Productions. I'll be returning to England with you.'

The words were like the passing of a death sentence. Had not LO promised he would protect her, look after her, keep her safe? And now, as judge and executioner in one, he had bound her fast and delivered her over to the enemy.

Like the villain in melodrama LO entered pat, on cue. Although he had only momentarily dropped into a limp because the knee was playing up – he wore a dressing-gown and had of course been playing Antrobus – she saw him in the fiendish guise of Richard III. He *was* Richard. She recoiled from him in horror.

With a typical Englishman's disregard for danger – with its accompanying under-estimation of all psychological pain – he either ignored or remained ignorant of what she was feeling. Perhaps his emotion towards Finch was, at this moment, greater than his emotion for her.

'Surprise, surprise,' he said to both of them, ambiguously playing himself off against them, and them off against each other. It was the two men who smiled and felt strong. Vivien stared at them like a rabbit caught in two sets of headlights, crossing as they met.

25

In the dressing-room a couple of nights later, LO, in a state of complete self-absorption, was removing his make-up with cold cream and tissues. Vivien had not begun to take off hers, nor had she started changing out of her Sabina costume.

She stared hard at him, to see if she could make him notice her. If he did, he made a deliberate point of not reacting. Failing that, she began to interrogate his image, asking herself at the same time how he could be so insensitive to her weaknesses. Did he really not perceive who *she* was? Not her name, her identity in the world, nor even her capabilities as an actress, but what she, in the price she had to pay for those gifts, possessed, the dark side of her radiance.

She took hold of one of Finch's flowers: God knows why she had not had them thrown out. But the flowers, they were neutral, weren't they? She examined the flower, its stamen, its petals. It was a lovely thing. But then she saw it as heavy, redolent with sinister implications – the bounty of Finch's arrival there in Brisbane.

She uttered a little stifled cry and dropped the flower in the bin. It gave its own little metallic shriek as it hit the tinny base.

LO had still not reacted. His make-up was at the smudging stage, with mascara and vermilion running together into rouge and lip-liner. As he rubbed in more of the cold-cream the distinctive lines vanished and his face dissolved into a featureless mask of dumb and nameless vacuity. Prior to the assumption of a new self.

'Come on, Viv. Are you going to change?'

'Into what? Cinderella?'

She then saw that his neglect of her had not in any way been studied; he had simply been completely involved in what he was doing. Her quirky fleeting tone startled him.

'Out of your costume.'

'I'll leave it on, I think.'

'Leave it on?'

'It'll help me play the part.'

Now it was his turn to scrutinise her in the mirror.

'What part?' he asked.

'Vamp, good-time girl, *sport*.' She spoke the last word in the Australian way, deliberately, thinking of Finch.

'Is something the matter?'

Instead of talking to her through the mirror, LO turned to face her.

'I told you not to do it, Larry. I told you to leave him here.'

She was giving him another chance. She paused, with baited breath. If only he . . .

'Don't be silly . . . I thought you'd be delighted that Finch is joining our little band.'

He snapped back into his mechanical self-absorption and returned to the scouring of his face with cleansing cream.

Later, at supper in their suite at Lennon's Hotel, Vivien still had not changed or taken off her make-up. The heat grew stifling and outside the window there began one of those electric storm displays which make the north and west of Australia seem like puppet stages for supernatural lightning effects. Rain drummed on the window-panes.

Vivien sat quietly in her beauty contest costume, sipping heavily from an often replenished wine glass. She viewed both Finch, who was at the supper, and LO, with suspicion and defeat. She even felt that June Kelly, who had also

213

joined them, might have become involved in conspiring with the men. There was little doubt in her mind at all that the young and vivacious girl, who had served LO loyally and earned everyone's respect, had been gossiping with Finch behind her back.

LO was expanding in his most relaxed, actor-manager's mood his future plans. June's eyes rested on Vivien, looked away, looked back again.

'This next year will be a bumper one,' he said. 'Binky Beaumont has just sent Vivien *A Streetcar Named Desire*. Do you know Tennessee Williams' work?'

'Yes . . . a bit,' answered the servile, forelock-tugging Finch.

'I wish I could talk Vivien out of it, but she's determined.'

All three of them looked at Vivien. Narrow as her thoughts were, she could see LO attempting to manoeuvre Finch into playing in *Streetcar* with her. They expected her to make a comment. She remained silent.

'Perhaps I could borrow the script?' asked Finch shiftily.

The manipulative LO rose: he had planted a seed.

Perhaps like those seeds that pass through the entrails of some Australian birds – so Vivien had been told – it would be more likely to stick to the bark where it had landed, and germinate.

'You're welcome,' said LO. He limped over to a table and picked up the bulky typescript of the play. Again, for a moment, LO's limp hallucinated her and transformed him into Crookback Dick. Vivien had to turn away.

'What's the play about?' asked June politely.

'You're the expert, Viv.'

Forced to take part in the conversation, Vivien stuttered.

'Er . . . it's about a woman – Blanche du Bois – who can't live the way the world wants her to . . . and loses her mind.'

Again this was a real, but withdrawn, vulnerable self who talked, not the brittle and vibrant Lady LO. She could tell she made LO impatient. He toyed with his glass, he fiddled with his knife as he went on further to explain in a halting and thoughtful way.

'I find it all rather sooty and unsavoury,' he said when she finished, 'but then the audiences don't mind a bit of smut.'

This made her stiffen and withdraw even more into the shadows, watched only by June. For Finch was smiling obediently at his lord and master, who, conscious of his fascination for the younger man, changed tack again.

'Can you do accents?' he asked Finch.

He answered drolly, 'I can do an Australian one pretty well.'

She could see how LO made concessions to the naïveté: the Australians might persecute and colonise the aboriginal in their own land, but to foreigners or when abroad they played their own, white version of the bushman to engage sympathy for their cultural backwardness. LO loved it.

'That's not so much an accent,' he chortled, 'as a collection of speech defects!'

Finch, not surprisingly, seemed a little alarmed. 'I was going to ask how they would take to my accent in England.'

'The critics will take their knives to it with great alacrity.'

'Is it very noticeable?'

'Not at all, my dear Finch. You have five very tiny problems.'

'Oh . . .' His face fell further, while LO enjoyed himself even more.

'That's one of them,' he answered, leaving the puzzle to eat its way further into Finch's worried features.

'The others are A, E, I, and U.'

Finch, fully toppled, said in a crestfallen tone, 'Oh.'

'No, not O,' insisted LO. He mimicked the flatness of Finch's vowel, making it sound as ironed out as a million years of soil erosion. 'But O.'

He put his arm round the younger man, who fed his instinct for self-renewal. Could it be, thought Vivien, that subconscious knowledge of what had happened between herself and Finch somehow boosted him too?

'Don't despair, Finch, I will have you speaking just like me a week after you get off the boat.'

She could not stand another moment. Dull despair again hemmed her in and she had to escape, whatever the cost to herself or to others. She was at the door before they noticed her. Or rather June noticed her, for the other pair were wrapped up in their mutual self-regard.

'Are you going, Vivien?' asked June.

'More or less. Part of me.'

She struggled with the door.

'You can't go out in that outfit, Puss,' came LO's pursuing, authoritative tone, flattening her again. She stared coldly and defiantly over at him, but he had decided, she could see, to take no notice. He turned back to his jokes with Finch, saying to her, 'Put on a coat at least.'

If this was not the ultimate ignoring of her! Her blind panic to flee changed to controlled fury. She went to the bedroom and fetched a coat.

'Of course, a coat . . .' she said in a slow, sing-song voice. 'I must put on a coat. I wouldn't want to be un-savoury.'

LO took absolutely no notice of her performance, but the others seemed scared and hurt. Vivien did not so much as waste a further glance on any of them.

'Is she all right?' asked June, who would have gone after her to help.

LO, forcing them both to remain and even relax, said sharply, 'She doesn't need applause for every performance.'

Only the torrential rain assuaged her feelings of betrayal. It cascaded down on her, bringing renewal and relief.

She turned up her lovely eager face to it, opening her mouth, gasping and drinking in as much as she could. Her coat, unsecured, gaped open, and the cooling flood penetrated her satin bodice and fish-net covered thighs, running down belly and legs and into her shoes.

She closed her eyes and stood still, the water washing

and sculpting her to an essence of her willowy, dancer-like self. A flash of lightning picked out all these exquisite details for a moment or two before returning them to the wet dark void.

26

Not more than a hundred yards away, Elsie, in another lavish hotel bedroom, logged the movements of the Old Vic tour and again, for the benefit of her English correspondent, engaged in consoling reflections on the nature of their Australian hosts.

She spotted this strange, ghost-like apparition, this transparency upon the blackness, like a lost yet dancing wave. She frowned as she tried to figure out what was going on outside. She left her desk and advanced to the window to have a closer look. Being a practical woman, she determined on an immediate course of action.

Out in the rain Vivien found her mood was changing. The water cooled her, but now had trickled in to corrode and chill her inner state. Her thoughts grew vexed, her isolation galled her. She muttered and fought with her coat which resisted her efforts to tear it off: a button refused to yield and kept slipping out of her frozen fingers. She cursed the solid English rainwear, with its buttons which would not easily rip off, its eyelets which refused to split. Some of her swearing was still directed at LO.

She took a firmer grip on the button fouling the sodden button hole. 'Good God, yes . . .' she was saying, 'put on one coat, put on two . . . people won't recognise us then for what we are.' She wrenched off a bottom button. 'No one will believe me when I denounce you.'

Vivien shook off the coat – whose identity to her was now clear – and dropped it in the slush at her feet.

Elsie Beyer hastened up.

'Vivien, why what's the matter, dear?' she called.

Vivien for a moment wondered who it was. Then she saw. Her mother. Oh no, Elsie.

'It's the rain . . . It's so clean . . .'

Elsie asked kindly, 'Is there something I can do?'

'There is, as a matter of fact, Elsie.' She went up close and put her face right next to hers. Elsie watched her warily. 'You can stop treating Laurence like some god . . . he's starting to believe you. Do you hear me?'

With her clenched fists she started to belabour Elsie on the shoulders. They were not damaging blows, but weak ones of utter prostration. Elsie withstood them without stepping back.

'He's just like the rest of us – a lost, weak, hopeless . . . sinner.'

To which Elsie countered, sensibly, 'You can't stay out here all night. You'll catch your death.'

Vivien half-collapsed into her arms. Elsie steered her back towards the lighted verandahs, muttering half to herself, half to Vivien, 'What a country . . . parched one moment, teeming the next.'

Vivien became like a waif. All her enmity towards Elsie had gone. She surrendered herself entirely into her care. She allowed herself totally to be succoured by the older woman whose feelings were quite melted by her pathetic condition.

'Let's get these wet things off.' She eased off the saturated tawdry costume of Sabina, frowning with irritation at the outlandishness of it all, and seeking from Vivien a sign that she could see it normally. But Vivien took no notice and just stared ahead.

'Tell me, Elsie,' she asked, 'do you think we ever, ever understand anybody else?'

Elsie watched her closely, unsure what she meant.

'Have you ever been in love?' asked Vivien.

'Y-e-s . . .'

'And did you understand him?'

219

'Mostly?'

Vivien sighed. 'You are very fortunate. I am surrounded by strangers. Intimate strangers.'

Elsie shuddered at the desperate anguish in her voice.

'There is something wrong with me. My love cannot turn men into friends . . . Intimacies with strangers is all I can fill my empty heart with.'

Elsie tried to ignore this and address herself to the task in hand, that of helping Vivien out of her wet clothes. Not an easy assignment; not lightened either by the sheer beauty of what became revealed when she divested Vivien of the last shreds of dripping underwear.

Not thinking, Vivien aided her, her thoughts far away, unaware of those resplendent gifts of maturity and suppleness her body owned, and which now the older woman contemplated with a dignified awe; without covetousness, envy, or any hint of sexuality. Vivien naked had become as amenable as an infant.

'Almost done, Vivien. I'll put you into one of my winter nighties. God knows why I brought them. Still, you'll be as warm as toast.'

Vivien sat down on the edge of the bed in the darkened room, stripped of illusion and expression, divested of paint and, finally, withdrawn and peaceful after being shaken by her inner storms – the woman she might have been had she not become an actress. She was more naked than her acting – or even her most intimate love-making – ever allowed her to be. For a moment or two she looked completely normal, no longer exciting, stimulating, provocative, but ordinarily natural, sexless – as if sex was, for always, a quality of mind and will. Here sat the woman who could have borne half a dozen children.

Elsie brought her a towel and gave her a brisk rub. She slipped over her shoulders the flannel nightie to drop its shapeless comfort over those over exposed thighs and calves. Elsie did up the top three buttons and helped her into bed.

'You pull the bedclothes up snug.'

She looked down at Vivien maternally.

'Would you like some cocoa?'

Vivien turned the question over in her mind as if she was not familiar with the language. She then nodded.

'Will you be all right while I slip down to the kitchen?'

Again Vivien nodded, this time more quickly, and smiled in gratitude. Some of her old self was returning to her.

'You just rest. There. I won't be long.'

Elsie smiled reassuringly from the door and left. Vivien continued to stare into infinity, the old maid's nightie buttoned up round her throat, and no man present to drive her to be something she was not.

The wind and rain continued to swirl and rage. The two actors gently swished the cognac round in their brandy glasses. June sipped a fruit juice from a large, condensation-dewed tumbler.

They were laughing at one of LO's jokes when a gust of wind puffed out the curtains and made them billow. Unlikely though it was – or perhaps likely, given the previous stifling heat – a window had been left open. June jumped to her feet to close it.

LO was instantly on his feet to help her – his gentlemanliness nearer the surface than Finch's: their combined efforts soon fastened the window. But its resistance and the sudden collapse threw June against LO, whose outstretched arms instinctively suddenly closed round her, wrapped across her breasts. A bright pulse of lightning flashed on their faces.

They sprang apart immediately, but neither was embarrassed. Finch seemed aware of the electricity which flowed through their bodies.

'Come on, Larry,' he called. 'Tell us the rest.'

LO went on with his rambling anecdote, acting out various parts, jumping over the bed, picking up room service props to help him. Sometimes they both laughed, sometimes they listened spellbound. In time the storm began to recede, with the thunder reduced to gibbering and muttering in the distance and the lightning cut down to faint, horizontal glimmerings.

A knock on the door interrupted their uproarious laughter. LO went and let in Elsie.

'Laurence, could I have a word with you?' Usually she was deferential towards him, but not tonight.

He frowned at her tone. He rose to conceal his irritation. The others chatted with each other as he took Elsie aside.

'What's happened now?'

Elsie patiently explained the situation, but LO would hardly let her go on, and apologised for the alarm Vivien caused. Usually it was he who hotly defended her.

They left the others who had overheard much that had passed.

'What should we do? Should we fetch a doctor?' He whispered to Elsie after he had tried to speak to Vivien. The indifferent, almost catatonic replies she made shocked him.

Elsie reassured him that she would sleep. 'She's exhausted. This has been coming on for days.' She stopped. LO said nothing. Elsie reacted as if she could not believe he had not noticed or understood.

'Surely you if anyone . . .' she appealed to him. Vivien had almost drifted off to sleep again. 'I've watched her on this tour,' she went on in a monotonously grave voice. 'I've watched her' – she sought the right word – 'cycles. Running wildly against the gale and not stopping till she drops.'

LO listened as if he had never experienced or thought anything she was saying.

'The utter exhaustion – the desolation – and all that follows. So regretful, so' – she said the next words with deep and tender feeling – 'terribly sorry. And then the painful healing until she's her normal self again, sweet

222

considerate, gracious, witty . . .' She turned round to look LO fully in the face. 'Until the next time.'

LO stood and listened to her like the rock of endurance.

'I know,' she went on, 'you try and protect her. I know what you put up with.'

'You've seen this before, haven't you?' he asked, his voice quavering a little. His meaning was plain.

'Yes.'

'As a nurse?'

'I'm certainly no expert.'

There. It had been said. LO, on the threshold of admitting to himself something he had never been prepared even to begin to countenance, wanted to hear it.

Elsie spoke with difficulty. 'Larry, I think Vivien is mentally ill.'

Her words almost crushed him.

'These moods, she doesn't control them . . .' Elsie sighed. 'And I'm not sure the doctors can help. All they would want to do was to smash her and mould her to some colder design. What she needs is to be preserved. She's such a . . . beautiful person.'

LO let out a long breath, rubbed his eyes and moved away from that pocket of the room that still held the memory of those words uttered by Elsie. Was he finally admitting to himself that sheer patience, manly fortitude, resilience, weren't enough?

After several moments he spoke. His tone was simple and appealing – the plea heartfelt.

'What can I do, Elsie?'

Elsie smiled softly. She thought for several moments. 'You could take her away somewhere. Somewhere calm and peaceful in the country. What she needs is a simple life. Away from crowds and parties – and all this fame – and adoration.'

But as she spoke an incredulous expression was slipping over LO's face – a bright fleecy cloud overtaking the bold and open clarity of his concern. It was as if Elsie was herself no longer being serious.

Elsie picked it up at once. Her next words were spoken with poignant irony. 'But of course you can't, can you? You're Laurence Olivier and Vivien Leigh.'

LO turned away. It was as if sentence had been passed, final and irrevocable. This time on him.

27

LO had one more meeting with Finch before they left Australia – Finch was no longer travelling with them, but joining them later in London. The day was fresh, the sky perfect blue, the sea a glittering and unruffled silver calm. They sat at a fish café on a pier.

Finch forked a mouthful of fish, swallowed it. LO was not hungry. He stared down at the sparkling waters. He was lost in thought.

'How's Vivien?' asked Finch after a while.

'Better, better,' LO barked back at him without conviction. He did not need any prompting to go on. 'It's this tour, Peter. It's been exhausting. She's at the end of her tether. We both are. We're walking corpses.'

LO prodded his fried whiting.

'She wants to see you,' he continued in a matter-of-fact tone.

Finch looked up at him from where he had been energetically engaged in eating squid.

'Is that a good idea?' he asked.

LO looked puzzled. 'Why ever not?'

'I don't think she wants me around any more.'

LO dismissed this idea with a gesture of the hand.

'Perhaps I shouldn't come to London,' Finch continued.

'Don't be silly,' said LO.

'I don't seem to have a good effect on her.'

But LO would not hear any more. 'Peter, don't blame yourself.'

'Why not? Why shouldn't I blame myself?'

'For what?' LO sat back and searched Finch's expression as if he found this unexpected.

Finch hesitated. 'For wanting my piece of her. Like everyone else . . .'

LO's dark brows grew furrowed. Was Finch making a specific confession or was this a fear for the future?

Finch added quickly, 'She's the most talented woman I've ever known.'

LO listened.

'Why do you never defend her?'

'But I do. All the time.'

'No, you don't. You make excuses.'

LO distanced himself from the younger actor. He did not seem touchy or proud at the comments. He sat there in the attitude of a listener or a learner: would he discover something about himself which he did not know?

'Perhaps I do. But not for her. I make excuses for me.'

Finch looked puzzled. He did not understand.

'What if I'm the cause, Peter? What if I'm her illness?'

The intimacy of the great man's confession touched Finch.

'Love,' LO went on. 'Such a selfish emotion. We talk of it like some hallowed gift and yet it is to ourselves we give it.' He leant forward and looked deeply and sincerely into Finch's dark eyes. 'I can't help her, Peter. I'm an interested party. A self-interested party. I want her to be well. I want her to flourish – to be the great actress she truly is . . . I want to protect her – and I can't even protect her from me . . .'

Finch's parting from Vivien was brief, and took place only an hour or two later. Vivien sat pale and fragile on the hotel terrace, sipping tea from a delicate bone-china cup. Finch approached her with a sheaf of white roses. She hardly seemed to notice his presence until he was a foot or two away. She was pleased, surprised – or so she registered – gave him a calm, passionless greeting, thanked him for his roses.

226

He was not able to say much. He wanted to reassure her that he had simply come for the job. If he underplayed his past involvement, she tried to undercut him even more by saying that she felt sorry she had been so awful to him.

He asked her to forget what had happened in Sydney. But if she had not already forgotten she seemed confused about geographical locations. Was she innocent, or was her faulty and selective memory just part of the act?

At least, in their last encounter, all mention of pain was omitted.

'I've said goodbye to Laurence,' Finch concluded. 'So I'll say goodbye to you.'

'See you in London, Peter.'

Confused by her ingenuousness, he repeated dully, 'Yes . . . see you in London.'

She smiled sweetly. She could have been a stranger.

The next afternoon they played *Richard III*. During the interval George Relph and Peter Cushing had to help LO back to the dressing-room, for he was in acute pain from his injured knee. Cushing expressed fear that it had never been this bad, but LO, placing his weight as gingerly as possible on the injured leg, told them not to fuss.

As they supported him into the dressing-room he fell against the door jamb and his face contorted at the sudden stab of pain. But he dismissed them summarily. He wanted to be on his own.

Vivien, still off from playing in *Richard III*, continued her meek Lady Bountiful act backstage, mucking in, this time, by ironing costumes in the wardrobe department.

Towards the end of the interval LO sat at his make-up mirror like death warmed up. June ministered to him, bringing him a hot drink which she placed on the table. He turned to her as he pulled on his black wig in preparation for the second half.

'Hot lemon. It's good for your throat . . . and a dash of something else.' This duly elicited from him a grateful smile.

'You've no idea what I turned my back on to come down here,' he said tersely.

'Oh I think I have,' she replied.

'It's been a disaster,' was all he could add.

'Not for the audience,' she answered, but looking into her eyes he could tell that she knew what he meant.

A 'five minutes' stage-call came through.

'I'll leave you to it,' said June.

'June?' LO called after her. She stopped by the door. 'Thank you.'

She smiled, touched at his gratitude. 'It's been a pleasure.' She gave him a big wink. 'Break a leg!'

His smile vanished as he turned back to face Richard III in the mirror. Here was the black-hearted villain he had to love. This was the monster he had to be. He had no alternative choice.

In that second part of the afternoon all the foul, soul-stained creature's venom and anguish seemed to become sublimated in love for Vivien as he cried, 'A horse! a horse! my kingdom for a horse!'

As he uttered this line LO swayed unsteadily on the makeshift crutch he had commissioned. He also supported himself on his sword, using it as a walking stick. Physical pain, mental torture, who knew the difference any longer?

'Withdraw, my lord,' advised Peter Cushing as Catesby. 'I'll help you to a horse.'

'Slave!' LO turned on him, spitting the words straight into his face.

> I have set my life upon a cast,
> And I will stand the hazard of the die.
> I think there be six Richmonds in the field;
> Five have I slain today instead of him.
> A horse! a horse! my kingdom for a horse!

With one supreme effort of will to master the stabbing sensation he lurched off to do battle. This afternoon he had determined he would, for once and all, kill off Richard

228

inside him. He would have his own revenge on the demon who had ravaged his love for Vivien.

The electrifying last minutes of the play advanced quickly to climax. Richmond, played by Cunningham, Stanley, and diverse others of the lords entered. LO raised his sword to defend himself and collapsed. From the floor he vainly struggled to ward off attacks with his sword and crutch as his assailants made to despatch him. He desperately crabbed along the stage, fighting like a wild thing. They stabbed him over and over again with their swords, as he writhed and squirmed to escape. At last, and in the throes of death he shuddered, releasing, in a series of sharp, orgasmic convulsions, his doppelgänger's evil genius. The dirty dog was dead.

The curtain fell. The applause broke and surged over the house, unchecked in its enthusiasm. The cast moved off the stage. LO lay on the boards, quite still, unable to rise.

'Dan! Peter!' he called hoarsely. 'Give me a hand. My leg's gone completely.'

Epilogue

LO had his knee operated on in New Zealand, the last lap of the tour, to have the cartilage removed. A few days after this they embarked on their voyage home aboard the SS *Corinthic*. In steady rain, watched by a small quayside crowd of well-wishers, LO was transported to the wharf in an ambulance. Lying on a stretcher, dressed in silk pyjamas and a blue dressing-gown, he was rigged up to a canvas sling. During this manoeuvre a bystander held an umbrella to shelter him from the rain, but not to much effect. Watched by the Old Vic Company who lined the aft of the *Corinthic*, LO was then hooked in his sling on to the steel hawser of a crane. A wharfie gave a wave to the crane driver, and the sling, its bottom reinforced by the two ambulance men who stood one at either end, rose up high to meet the towering aft of the vessel.

LO felt himself soaring into the sky. He peeked out uncertainly and gave a little wave to the crowd, who waved and cheered back, squinting in the rain for a last sight of the legendary actor. As he smoothly floated over the side of the ship to land on the top-most deck he disappeared like a god being transported back to his home in the heavens.

They sailed eighteen days before they reached Panama City. During most of that time Olivier sat against a pile of cushions on the bed in his stateroom. His right leg was encased in plaster, and his mood was mostly thoughtful and melancholic as he went over in his mind the events of the past few months, particularly that of his sacking from the Old Vic.

Vivien tackled him directly on this subject one day. She had fully recovered – for the time being. Again she had become beautiful, and swam, as the weather across the Pacific warmed up, in the ship's canvas pool. At night she would appear in the dining room in the simplest of gowns: a hush would descend as everyone turned to look at her.

'You can't continue to work for them,' she said to LO.

'I've got another six months of my contract.'

'Why show them any loyalty? They've shown none to you.'

He made an empty gesture.

'You've become too big for them and they couldn't bear it,' she went on.

He interrupted in a mournful tone which showed how strongly he felt critical of himself: 'You think it's all a waste of time?'

'No,' she answered. 'You were right to make a stand. You did it for the good of the company. What they did, they did for power. You want power, yes. We all do. Power to do our work as we see it. Not power for power's sake.'

'I'm not sure which galls me more. My losing or their ingratitude.'

Her face flushed with sympathy towards him.

'I've lost my base, Bibs. And I'm not used to losing.'

'We all lose, Larry. It's in the scheme of things.' And she sighed as if she now meant the statement to refer to herself. 'What do you want most in the world?'

LO looked at her, ready to laugh, but saw she meant the question in earnest. 'To get through the next ten years of work,' he answered seriously.

'What are you working for?' she pursued her catechism.

'The future . . . the theatre . . . Myself . . .' And he added, in a more cautious tone, 'My sanity.'

'I work hard, too, you know.'

'Darling, you work too hard – at everything.'

234

'Because I *want* everything. I want perfection. The unattainable. I always have. I wanted that for us.'

He frowned at the odd interposition of the past tense.

'. . . wanted?'

'To be in love forever.'

Perhaps he did not notice the resolved expression on her face, which came from the fact that she was trying to tell him something. Or if he did, perhaps he wanted to avoid recognition, and merely to enjoy the game of words.

'How long's forever?' he asked more lightly.

'For as long as we're remembered.'

LO continued talking in the spirit of the game. He adopted a tone of mock disappointment. 'Oh . . . is that all?'

'Fame or happiness. Which do you choose?'

He enjoyed the conundrum. Vivien was really her old self.

'What's the difference?' he answered flippantly, meaning that to him both were the same, or one could not be had without the other. He grinned at her, to include her in his boyish complicity, but she did not yield, never wavering from the penetrating stare she gave him.

'This play of course is a tragedy,' he was telling the company who had assembled for a read-through of the new play by Jean Anouilh they were to perform on their return to London. He sat with his leg in a plaster cast propped up on a stool in front of him. There clung about him an indeterminate but almost cosmic sense of fatigue and oppression.

'. . . and I would like to suggest that you keep at the back of your minds the whole time you're playing it – a feeling of doom. If you keep it here' – he drew the line with his hand from the top of his head to his neck about three inches from the back of his head – 'with the rest of your head you can feel much lighter. It will help you with some of the lines which may otherwise make no sense . . . For this play you see' – he spoke with almost off-hand

235

simplicity, in a light flat voice, giving them a thin, wan smile – 'like life, has two realities. What people *say* and what people *feel* . . . Shall we begin?'

Playscripts were rustled, throats cleared, spectacles or other items of dress adjusted as the company settled down for the read-through.

'Well here we are,' LO began in the role of Chorus. He made a gesture to acknowledge the others. 'These people are about to act out for you the story of Antigone. That thin little creature sitting by herself staring straight ahead, seeing nothing is Antigone . . .'

Vivien's eyes lifted from her script to look at LO.

'She is thinking. She is thinking she is going to die.'

Vivien turned round to where Dan Cunningham sat and gave him a small, sad smile.

'Antigone is young. She would much rather live than die. But there is no help for it. When your name is Antigone, there is only one part you can play; and she will have to play hers through to the end.'

As time aboard the *Corinthic* turned from days into weeks the company increased their drinking. After the rigours of the tour everyone needed to let their hair down. Drink provided the most obvious safety-valve. Elsie started again to complain to LO of the company's wild and scurrilous behaviour.

Vivien started to grow bored again. At first the constant replenishment of her high-style cocktails was enough to satisfy her, but then her flirtation with Dan Cunningham gained new intensity.

One night she jitterbugged with him in the ship's dining-room. This time LO, up and alert again, had come along and sat, his leg propped on its stool, watching the pair. Sipping wine from a glass he contemplated, with the some-what aloof view of *Antigone*'s chorus – Cunningham and Vivien's teasing and provocative performance.

'Sorry you can't join in?' said Elsie who had spotted LO's isolation and come over to where he sat.

He grinned. 'Not at all. Sometimes,' he pointed to his leg in plaster, 'this thing's a blessing.'

'How are rehearsals?'

'Fine . . . Fine . . .' he said distractedly, wondering if he ought not to have a serious talk with Vivien about her flirtation.

'It's such a depressing play.'

'Yes,' he agreed with gloomy mirth. 'I don't know why I like it so much. I suppose it has a certain – symmetry.'

Elsie gave him a sad, understanding smile.

'Another drink?'

He handed her his empty glass. 'And another and another . . . Why don't you join me, Elsie?'

'Why? Are you coming apart?' she countered, which took LO by surprise because Elsie was not given to making jokes.

'It's a joke, isn't it?' she added.

He smiled at her. 'Yes Elsie, I think it is.'

She headed away to fetch more wine. He smiled and returned to watching Vivien and Cunningham. Their energetic and seductive dance now swelled into the enormity of a mating ritual, utterly unambiguous in its gestures. But instead of mounting jealousy and indignation LO felt exhaustion. What was the point, any more, in trying to stop her being what she was? He smiled sadly and repeated to himself lines from *Antigone* which he knew already but had hardly made any effort to study.

'Tragedy is clean, it is restful, it is flawless. In a tragedy, nothing is in doubt and everyone's destiny is known. That makes for tranquility. There is a sort of fellow-feeling among characters in a tragedy: he who kisses is as innocent as he who gets killed; it's all a matter of what part you are playing . . .'

Later that evening, after the dance, George, Peter and Terence carried LO up to his stateroom. LO had drunk himself into a state of semi-stupefaction. The porters behaved noisily and drunkenly.

'Don't you know, you're lucky it's your right leg, Larry,' said Cushing.

'What . . . ?'

'Well . . . there was nothing wrong with the other one was there . . . ?'

They all dissolved into drunken laughter.

'Thank you everyone – you've been very kind,' said Vivien, when they had deposited their load on to the bed.

'Would you like us to undress him, Vivien?' asked Dan.

'That I'll do myself.'

'Good-night, Larry,' said an exceedingly merry Morgan. 'Pleasant dreams.' He turned to the others. 'By the way, do you know he's plastered?'

They groaned at the silly observation and dissolved again into laughter as Vivien herded them out and closed the door after them. She smiled to herself and turned to LO. She had him all to herself again.

He was sitting up in bed wearing a silk pyjama top. From the chair in which she combed her long, sleek hair Vivien surveyed him through the dressing-table mirror.

He watched her. He wanted nothing more than to take her passionately and prove his love. But he could not. He was not prepared yet to take any liberties with his leg: he knew his own living tissue, it was the raw material of his art. He knew he was not ready.

He spoke after a long time.

'Why do you do it, Vivien?'

All he could do was liberate his insecurities.

'Do what?' she said sharply turning round.

'You know what I mean,' he said irritably.

'I have no idea.'

Facing her he found it more difficult to speak. It was not something he would normally bring up.

'Flirt like that . . . with Cunningham.'

'I wasn't flirting. I was dancing.'

LO felt uncomfortable. But for the leg, and the dependant habit of mind it had brought, he would not be saying

238

this. It was as if his body had jumped on the bandwagon of his unhappiness and now taken the reins.

'Wasn't I?' Vivien challenged him.

He shifted position on the bed, as if to make a point of how his knee was to blame.

But Vivien's expression suddenly changed, adopting a chastened air.

'I don't always know the difference.'

He stroked his neck. He wondered what to say next.

'I'm worried about you, Viv.'

'I know . . .'

'I wish I could help.'

'You're a great man, Larry, but you can't do everything.'

Her tone was so even-handed that he couldn't be sure he could detect any irony. He just felt anguish.

'I know there's something wrong with me. But I don't know what it is. I'm not like other people.'

'Who wants to be like other people . . . ?' he echoed her with an attempt at encouragement, but not much conviction. Just then he hungered after the safe and ordinary.

They sat in lone silence, separate and alone.

'I wish I had a clean disease . . . like cancer.'

He refused to contemplate the enormity of this.

'Things change,' he said. 'They'll be the same again.'

'No.'

'Vivien, we've got to try. We can't just let it go. We've got much more together than apart.'

'It isn't enough.'

'It's enough for me.'

She looked at him. Maybe so, but not enough for her. Like Antigone she wanted everything of life. She wanted it then and there, total, complete, otherwise she rejected it. She would not be moderate. She would not be satisfied with the bit of cake he offered her, if she promised him to be a good little girl. If not, she wanted to die.

And if he objected, it was he, after all, who had cast her in the role.

LO now asked hesitantly, 'Is there . . . is there someone else?'

'No,' she answered. 'It's us . . . There's something I must tell you . . . I don't love you any more. It happened . . . I first saw it' – her own voice adopted an almost disbelieving tone – 'in Australia.'

LO stared over at his wife, scrutinising her face and trying to ascertain how much of her condition was acting, how much real. He could not find the answer. His face began to work as the full force of her confession struck home, utterly devastating him.

He opened his mouth to speak but nothing came. There was no escape. In melodrama you could argue and struggle in the hope of escape. In tragedy, where there was no longer the chance, argument was gratuitous.

They all had to play the parts they had been given.